PENGUIN STUDENT EDITIONS

THE FOX AND OTHER STORIES

David Herbert Lawrence (1885–1930) was born into a miner's family in Eastwood, Nottinghamshire. He attended Beauvale Board School and Nottingham High School, and trained as an elementary schoolteacher at Nottingham University College. He taught in Croydon from 1908. His first novel, *The White Peacock*, was published in 1911, just a few weeks after the death of his mother, to whom he had been extremely close. His career as a schoolteacher was ended by serious illness at the end of 1911.

In 1912 Lawrence went to Germany with Frieda Weekley, the German wife of a professor at the University College of Nottingham. They were married on their return to England in 1914. Lawrence had published *Sons and Lovers* in 1913; but *The Rainbow*, completed in 1915, was suppressed, and for three years he could not find a publisher for *Women in Love*, completed in 1917.

After the First World War, Lawrence lived abroad with Frieda in Italy, Sri Lanka, Australia, New Mexico and Mexico. They returned to Europe in 1925, settling in Italy again, where he finished *Lady Chatterley's Lover*. This, his last novel, was published in 1928, but did not appear in its complete form in England and America for thirty years. The tuberculosis which had first been diagnosed in Mexico was becoming more serious by this time, and in a last attempt to find a cure Frieda took him to Germany and then France. He died aged forty-four in Vence, in the south of France. After his death Frieda wrote that 'What he had seen and felt and known he gave in his writing to his fellow men, the splendour of living, the hope of more and more life . . . a heroic and immeasurable gift.'

Lawrence's life may have been short, but he produced an amazing body of work: novels, stories, poems, plays, essays, translations, paintings, letters (over five thousand of which survive) and travel books. His travel books, which often contain a great deal of personal narrative, are *Twilight in Italy* (1916), *Sea and Sardinia* (1921), *Mornings in Mexico* (1927) and *Sketches of Etruscan Places* (1932).

Valerie Durow recently completed a doctoral thesis on the modern British novel. She is currently administering post-graduate courses and research programmes in the School of English Studies, University of Nottingham.

Ronald Carter is Professor of Modern English Language in the School of English Studies, University of Nottingham. He has published widely in the field of language and literature studies and applied linguistics and English teaching. He is the co-author with John McRae of *The Penguin Guide to English Literature* (1996) and *The Routledge History of Literature in English: Britain and Ireland* (1997).

John McRae is Special Professor of Language in Literature Studies in the School of English Studies at the University of Nottingham. He is the author and editor of more than forty books, including, with Ronald Carter, *The Penguin Guide to English Literature*. He has lectured in over forty countries worldwide.

Penguin Student Editions
Series editors: Ronald Carter and John McRae

Other titles in this series:
Animal Farm by George Orwell
The Beach by Alex Garland
Cal by Bernard Mac Laverty
The Call of the Wild by Jack London
A Christmas Carol by Charles Dickens
Dubliners by James Joyce
Emma by Jane Austen
The Garden Party and Other Stories by Katherine Mansfield
A Good Man in Africa by William Boyd
The Hound of the Baskervilles by Arthur Conan Doyle
The Importance of Being Earnest by Oscar Wilde
Jane Eyre by Charlotte Brontë
Lord Arthur Savile's Crime and Other Stories by Oscar Wilde
Nineteen Eighty-Four by George Orwell
A Passage to India by E. M. Forster
Pride and Prejudice by Jane Austen
The Strange Case of Dr Jekyll and Mr Hyde by Robert Louis Stevenson
Ten Short Stories by Roald Dahl
The Time Machine by H. G. Wells
The Turn of the Screw by Henry James
Wide Sargasso Sea by Jean Rhys

D. H. Lawrence

The Fox and Other Stories

Edited by Valerie Durow

PENGUIN BOOKS

PENGUIN BOOKS

Published by the Penguin Group
Penguin Books Ltd, 27 Wrights Lane, London w8 5tz, England
Penguin Putnam Inc., 375 Hudson Street, New York, New York 10014, USA
Penguin Books Australia Ltd, Ringwood, Victoria, Australia
Penguin Books Canada Ltd, 10 Alcorn Avenue, Toronto, Ontario, Canada m4v 3b2
Penguin Books India (P) Ltd, 11, Community Centre, Panchsheel Park, New Delhi – 110 017, India
Penguin Books (NZ) Ltd, Private Bag 102902, NSMC, Auckland, New Zealand
Penguin Books (South Africa) (Pty) Ltd, 5 Watkins Street, Denver Ext 4, Johannesburg 2094, South Africa

Penguin Books Ltd, Registered Offices: Harmondsworth, Middlesex, England

This collection first published in Penguin Student Editions 2001
1

Editorial matter copyright © Valerie Durow, 2001
All rights reserved

The moral right of the editor has been asserted

Set in 9.75/12.5 pt PostScript Monotype Plantin
Typeset by Rowland Phototypesetting Ltd, Bury St Edmunds, Suffolk
Printed in England by Clays Ltd, St Ives plc

Contents

Introduction

'In the work of D. H. Lawrence . . . is found the profoundest research into human nature.'

– T. S. Eliot

D. H. Lawrence was born in 1885 in Eastwood, Nottinghamshire. His father was a coal miner and, for a time, his mother ran a small shop to supplement the family income. Lawrence's mother, who felt that she had married beneath her, was determined that her son should not follow his father down the mine. She was ambitious for her son and encouraged him to study. Lawrence attended Nottingham High School and Nottingham University College and qualified as a teacher, a career that was ended in 1911 by illness. In 1912 Lawrence eloped to Germany with Frieda Weekley, the wife of his former modern languages tutor. They married in 1914 after Frieda's divorce. The Lawrences travelled widely throughout Europe and also to Ceylon, Australia and New Mexico. D. H. Lawrence died of tuberculosis in Vence in 1930 at the age of forty-four.

Despite the brevity of his life, Lawrence produced a great amount of work, not only such major novels as *Sons and Lovers*, *The Rainbow* and *Women in Love*, but essays, tales, stories, poems, plays, literary criticism, travel writings, translations and letters. The five stories contained in this book span Lawrence's writing career.

'Odour of Chrysanthemums' and 'Her Turn' are early stories and were written soon after Lawrence left Nottinghamshire to teach in Croydon. Like his novel *Sons and Lovers*, both are set in the Nottinghamshire mining community of his youth, and deal with problematic relationships, notably those between husband and wife. Lawrence was one of the first writers to portray the working class from within its ranks.

'Her Turn', rejected for publication by the *Daily News* in March 1912, is narrated in a tone of amused tolerance, and is a story in which Lawrence portrays a woman in an extremely positive fashion. It presents a marriage, a second one for the man, which is generally happy as 'there was between them that truce which is never held between a man and his first woman'. The miner, Radford, is shown not as mean-spirited, but as genial and popular – 'big, naïve and very courteous' to his wife and the neighbour women, with a 'fresh interest in life [that] made his presence always agreeable'. His wife is sleek, sly and cat-like, but significantly not a shrew. Domestic economics are at the heart of the tale. Although related in a light-hearted way, the woman's determination that the man should part with some of his strike-pay does highlight that wives are solely dependent on their husbands. Further, Radford's carefree visits, whether money is scarce or not, to the public house show the separate life that a man is able to lead away from the problems of the home. Radford, it seems, is fond of puzzles, but he is not able to solve the one with which his wife presents him in her efforts to obtain the strike-pay – the puzzle of the new household items. Using her savings, she buys items that she cleverly demonstrates are necessities. Her husband's response is pure bemusement – 'Well, this is a corker!', 'Well, this is a winder!' The smug satisfaction displayed by the wife provokes an almost automatic and uncontrolled, violent reaction in the man which reveals the tension in the relationship: 'A wave of anger came over him, blinding him. But he waited and waited. Suddenly, his arm leapt up, the fist clenched, and his eyes blazed at her.' However, no blows are struck and the man retreats to the garden. The woman's victory is assured and the man hands over the strike-pay. The final image that Lawrence leaves us with is one of the woman in control, as she generously hands back some money to the grateful man. Overall, we gain the sense of a settled and balanced relationship but, as the title suggests, this time it was 'her turn' to gain the upper hand and assert her individuality.

'Odour of Chrysanthemums' was first published in the *English Review* in June 1911. Although the setting is similar, this story is much darker in tone than 'Her Turn'. Lawrence explores alienation in a relationship, an alienation that is mirrored in the environment. It begins with a panoramic view which then narrows and focuses on one small, family scene. A sense of decay and dread is immediately created. The industrialized landscape is shown as unlovely and threatening: 'In the open, the smoke from the engine sank and cleaved to the rough grass . . . The pit-bank loomed up beyond the pond, flames like red sores licking its ashy sides, in the afternoon's stagnant light.' The fields are 'dreary and forsaken' and even in the cottage garden an element of threat can be detected as 'a large bony vine clutched at the house, as if to claw down the tiled roof' and raspberry-canes rise 'like whips'. The 'dishevelled pink chrysanthemums', 'wintry primroses' and 'ragged cabbages' lend an air of sadness to the scene.

We are given the impression that Elizabeth Bates, the chief character in the story, is a strong woman. She is described as 'a tall woman of imperious mien, handsome, with definite black eyebrows'. Her marriage is an unhappy one, with her husband preferring to drink all night in the public house rather than return home after work. However, we are only able to see things from Elizabeth's initially antagonistic point of view, as Walter, her husband, is effectively an 'absent presence' throughout the story. On this occasion, we see Elizabeth getting increasingly angry, 'evident in the stern unbending of her head'. She speaks 'bitterly', 'irritably' and 'in a tone of fine bitter carelessness'. As the family await the return of the father, Lawrence creates a mood of suspense, and the early anger gives way to unease and fear. After the children are put to bed, 'the room was strangely empty, with a tension of expectancy', and Elizabeth's 'anger was tinged with fear'. Finally, her husband is brought home, not drunk but dead, killed in an accident in the pit. As she and her mother-in-law wash Walter's body, Elizabeth is forced into the realization that she never really knew or understood her husband. In the final part of the story, Lawrence presents, through Elizabeth's consciousness and through narrative comment, a powerful analysis of an alienated relationship:

Life with its smoky burning gone from him, had left him apart and utterly alien to her. And she knew what a stranger he was to her. In her womb was ice of fear, because of this separate stranger with whom she had been living as one flesh. Was this what it all meant – utter, intact separateness, obscured by heat of living? In dread she turned her face away. The fact was too deadly. There had been nothing between them . . 'Who am I? What have I been doing? I have been fighting a husband who did not exist. *He* existed all the time. What wrong have I done? What was that I have been living with? There lies the reality, this man.' – And her soul died in her for fear: she knew she had never seen him, he had never seen her, they had met in the dark and had fought in the dark, not knowing whom they met nor whom they fought.

She comes to recognize that there were faults on both sides: 'For his look was other than hers, his way was not her way. She had denied him what he was – she saw it now. She had refused him as himself. – And this had been her life, and his life. – She was grateful to death, which restored the truth.' Now humbled, Elizabeth has to acknowledge that she had very little to offer Walter – 'how awful he must have felt it to be a husband' – and she can make 'no reparation'; just as he was suffocated in the mine, in life he was suffocated in the relationship and rejected by his wife. The ending of the story is ambivalent; there is obviously hope for the future in the children, both born and unborn, but Lawrence's final image is one of submission and resignation: 'She knew she submitted to life, which was her immediate master. But from death, her ultimate master, she winced with fear and shame.'

Throughout the story is the recurring image of the chrysanthemums, symbolically representative of hope and despair. Described early in the story as 'ragged wisps' and 'wan flowers', they seem to be associated with sadness and decay. Being autumnal flowers, they are associated with the end of summer and the approach of winter and here they are linked to evening, the end of the day, and also, inevitably, the end of Elizabeth's relationship with her husband. Yet they were present at happier occasions, when Elizabeth embarked on married life, and when her children were born: '"It was chrysanthemums when I married him, and chrysanthemums when you were born, and the first time they ever brought him home drunk, he'd got brown chrysanthemums in his button-hole."' But the odour of chrysanthemums is all-pervasive. It is of some note that Lawrence uses the word 'odour' rather than the more attractive 'scent' or 'perfume', as this suggests that the faintly musty smell of these flowers is more fittingly associated with death – 'there was a cold, deathly smell of chrysanthemums'.

'You Touched Me' and *The Fox* are similar in theme. Basically, both deal with a male interloper disrupting a female household, captivating and then finally marrying one of the women. Lawrence still examines tensions within relationships, but there is more complexity and ambivalence, and there seems at times to be an almost sinister aspect to these stories.

'You Touched Me' is the shorter story. It was first published in the collection of stories *England, My England,* in 1922. In its description of Pottery House and its surroundings, it begins with an air of barrenness, sterility and decay. The yard is 'desolate', the pottery is no longer in production, so there is no life, no vitality, and this is emphasized by the stark, repetitive description:

No more the great crates with yellow straw showing through, stood in stacks by the packing shed. No more the drays drawn by great horses rolled down the hill with a high load. No more the pottery-lasses in their clay-coloured overalls, their faces and hair splashed with fine grey mud, shrieked and larked with the men. All that was over.

Similarly there is an air of barrenness about the two 'old maids', Emmie and Matilda, whose lives are 'grey and dreary' and whose marriages have been prevented by a lack of suitors of a suitable social class. The feeling of decay is reinforced in the illness of their father, Ted Rockley. Into this atmosphere of decline comes a vital and regenerating life-force in the shape of Hadrian. In Hadrian, Lawrence has created an ambiguous figure. The reader is unsure of what to think or feel about him. The women call him 'sly', but we are told that 'he was merely cautious'. He is described as an 'indomitable, dangerous charity boy' and as possessing 'some of the neatness, the reserve, the underground quality of the rat'. Yet this negative view is counterbalanced by reference to a more positive trait, courage: 'he had perhaps the ultimate courage, the most unquenchable courage of all'.

Although Matilda resists the offer of marriage, made on Hadrian's behalf by her father, she finally acquiesces. The fact that her father has threatened to change his will in Hadrian's favour if she does not has to be taken into consideration. Their relationship appears to have little to do with love and affection, but rather more to do with compulsion. Hadrian's desire for the marriage seems to be a result of Matilda mistakenly entering his bedroom and touching him, which he takes as some sort of symbolic claim upon him. Touch was important to Lawrence, as evidenced in the letter which he wrote to Blanche Jennings on 15 December 1908: 'Somehow I think we come into knowledge (unconscious) of the most vital part of the cosmos through touching things . . . Such a touch is the connection between the vigorous flow of two lives.' Matilda is obviously compelled out of financial reasons. After agreeing to the marriage, Matilda is 'silent and unmoved' and Hadrian is 'quiet and satisfied, and nipped with fear also'.

In the story, Lawrence addresses aspects of social class and ambition. Although Hadrian was adopted by the Rockleys – 'an ordinary boy from a Charity Home, with ordinary brownish hair and ordinary bluish eyes and of ordinary rather cockney speech' – he is still considered a member of a lower class; his commonness is commented upon by Emmie and his 'cocksure manliness' seems to disconcert both sisters. Lawrence appears to suggest that Hadrian can be seen as a regenerating working-class force who has the potential to re-invigorate the sterile middle-class household. He is 'charged with plebeian energy'. Yet there is ambivalence here too. Although Hadrian passionately speaks out 'against the propertied classes', he appears to want to join them and wield power: 'he badly wanted to be an employer himself, not one of the employed'. Even the marriage is dominated by economic considerations, but in a complex way that has to do with both money and power: 'But he knew, in his subtle, calculating way, that it was not for money he wanted Matilda. He wanted both the money and Matilda. But he told himself the two desires were separate, not one. He could not do with Matilda, *without* the money. But he did not want her *for* the money.'

The similar themes of *The Fox* are explored in greater detail as it is a much longer story. *The Fox*, variously described as a novella, short novel, novelette and *nouvelle*, was first published in an American magazine, *The Dial*, in four instalments between May and August 1922. The first British publication of *The Fox* was in 1923, by Martin Secker. It was published, together with two other novellas, under the title *The Ladybird*.

Lawrence begins with the description of the life of two women, March and Banford, on their 'desolate little farm'. Again, the image is one of sterility, stagnation and barrenness:

They were neither of them young: that is, they were near thirty. But they certainly were not old. They set out quite gallantly with their enterprise. They had numbers of chickens . . . also some ducks; also two heifers in the fields. One heifer, unfortunately, refused absolutely to stay in the Bailey Farm closes . . . So this heifer they sold in despair. Then, just before the other beast was expecting her first calf, the old man died, and the girls, afraid of the coming event, sold her in a panic, and limited their attentions to fowls and ducks . . . Fowls did not flourish at Bailey Farm.

Furthermore, the impression is gained that the farm is not overly important to the women; they are middle-class women 'playing' at being farmers. Both are city girls: March had 'learned carpentry and joinery at the evening classes in Islington'. They believed that 'life was not made merely to be slaved away' and 'both Banford and March disbelieved in living for work alone'.

Although lesbian implications might be detected in March and Banford's relationship, there is nothing to suggest that Lawrence considers the friendship repulsive or ugly. For example, when Banford is upset, March comforts her 'with wonderful gentleness and tenderness'. Banford is a 'warm, generous soul', March has 'a strange magnanimity' and both are 'usually the best of friends'. However, what Lawrence does suggest is that, like the farm, the friendship is sterile and non-productive – 'they seemed to have to live too much off themselves' – and that Banford's love for March is parasitic and jealously possessive. Banford, 'a thin, frail little thing', is fearful of life, of Nature and of the virile interloper, Henry Grenfel, who, possessing the 'brightness of abundant health', disrupts their lives:

Banford was offended. For all his suave courtesy and soft voice, the youth seemed to her impudent. She did not like to look at him. She did not like to meet his clear, watchful eyes, she did not like to see the strange glow in his face, his cheeks with their delicate fine hair, and his ruddy skin that was quite dull and yet which seemed to burn with a curious heat of life. It made her feel a little ill to look at him: the quality of his physical presence was too penetrating, too hot.

Henry's position is ambivalent. Is he hero or predator? His imagery is linked to that of the fox: 'But to March he was the fox. Whether it was the thrusting forward of his head, or the glisten of fine whitish hairs on the ruddy cheek-bones, or the bright, keen eyes, that can never be said: but the boy was to her the fox, and she could not see him otherwise.' Just as the animal has transfixed March, so does Henry: 'He was identified with the fox – and he was here in full presence. She need not go after him any more. There in the shadow of her corner she gave herself up to a warm, relaxed peace, almost like sleep, accepting the spell that was on her.' But the fox's position is not clear; it is both hunter and hunted, as is demonstrated when Henry kills the animal. It is a potent symbol of masculinity, yet at the same time is characterized as cunning and sly. Similarly, Henry's qualities are linked with those of the fox. He is 'young and vigorous', yet 'sly and subtle', his smile is 'a cunning little flame'.

Like the relationship between Hadrian and Matilda, that between March and Henry also seems to be one of domination and compulsion. Yet things are not so clear-cut. There is some sense of affection, although suppressed, as Henry knows that if he speaks to March of love, she would ridicule his 'tomfoolery'. There is also a sense of a developing relationship, and the compulsion seems to be apparent in both man and woman, although the domination is solely on the man's side. Henry watches March and 'her dark eyes made something rise in his soul, with a curious elate excitement'; he is 'inevitably impelled'. Similarly, March finds that Henry's voice has a 'curious power over her'. When Henry considers marriage, it is less an outright decision on his part, more of a revelation: '. . . why not marry March? He stood still in the middle of the field for some moments, the dead rabbit hanging still in his hand, arrested by this thought. His mind waited in amazement – it seemed to calculate – and then he smiled curiously to himself in acquiescence.' It is perhaps significant that Henry has just caught the rabbit when this thought occurs to him, because disquieting images of domination and conflict appear in his pursuit of March. It is to be 'a slow, subtle battle', 'he would have to catch her as you catch a deer or a woodcock', 'it was as a young hunter, that he wanted to bring down March as his quarry, to make her his wife'. After initial resistance, March gives in. The battle is then between Henry and Banford for March's affections.

The most problematic aspects of the story are Banford's 'murder' and the ending. Can we condone Henry's actions and still consider him hero and liberator of March? The narrator gives us no clue how to judge the incident, but we do get the impression that Henry knows exactly what he is doing. He is after all an expert tree-feller and a calm and careful hunter who has recently identified Banford as a 'nasty little creature' and who has 'in his heart . . . decided her death'. Is Banford's stubbornness to blame, her refusal to heed Henry's warnings? But his request for her to move is not made very forcefully; indeed, we are told that he wills her not to move – 'his heart held perfectly still, in the terrible pure will that she should not move'. Is it the fault of a decadent England, which has stung Henry with poison? Or is it possible to view Banford's death symbolically, merely as an act in a tragic drama, with her death representing the death of selfish, possessive love, allowing March to be freed and regeneration and renewal to take place?

There seems to be no easy or satisfactory interpretation which totally justifies Henry's actions. Banford is on the whole portrayed sympathetically; she is never presented as an evil character, merely slightly delicate, a little selfish and somewhat clinging.

Similarly, the ending of the story also presents problems. Although married, both March and Henry demonstrate unease about the relationship and about the future:

And he was . . . foiled. He realized that though he was married to her and possessed her in every possible way, apparently, and though she *wanted* him to possess her, she wanted it, she wanted nothing else, now, still he did not quite succeed . . . Sometimes he thought bitterly that he ought to have left her. He ought never to have killed Banford. He should have left Banford and March to kill one another.

March's thoughts are equally, or possibly more, disturbing, especially as she is an older, more experienced woman. Rather than seeing her marriage as some sort of partnership, she feels that she is being made not only passive and submissive, but is being totally submerged:

And she could not quite accept the submergence which his new love put upon her . . . No, he wouldn't let her exert her love towards him. No, she had to be passive, to acquiesce, and to be submerged under the surface of love. She had to be like the seaweeds she saw as she peered down from the boat, swaying forever delicately under water, with all their delicate fibrils put tenderly out upon the flood, sensitive, utterly sensitive.

The Fox is often described as a version of the 'Sleeping Beauty' fairy tale, where a handsome prince awakens a beautiful sleeping princess. While it is undeniable that March seems to be in some sort of trance before Henry's arrival, as she is described as 'always lapsing into this odd, rapt state' and 'spell-bound', it would seem that the 'prince', finding his bride awakened, wishes to put her back to sleep again: 'He wanted her asleep, at peace in him. He wanted her at peace, asleep in him.' Again Henry's desire for male domination rises to the surface: 'He wanted to veil her woman's spirit, as Orientals veil the woman's face. He wanted her to commit herself to him, and to put her independent spirit to sleep. He wanted to take away from her all her effort, all that seemed her very *raison d'être*.' Yet March still strives for independence and fights against his sleep-inducing influence: 'She *would* be an independent woman to the last. But she was so tired, so tired of everything. And sleep seemed near. And there was such rest in the boy.' Hope for Henry appears to lie in the 'New World', not the old: 'He believed that as they crossed the seas, as they left this England which he so hated, because in some way it seemed to have stung him with poison, she would go to sleep. She would close her eyes at last, and give in to him.'

The ending is ambiguous; there is no satisfactory close to the story. Although Lawrence brings his characters to the brink of a new life, he seems unwilling or unable to envisage or explore this new life or its possibilities, and thus the reader, like the characters, is left to some extent in a state of limbo. Both characters are looking out to sea, contemplating the future away from England in Canada, but March is still struggling against the impulse to acquiesce, to submit, to sleep: 'And her eyelids dropped with the slow motion, sleep weighing them unconscious. But she pulled them open again to say: "Yes, I may. I can't tell. I can't tell what it will be like over there."'

'The Flying Fish', the final story in the collection, is a lyrical and visionary piece. It is an unfinished fragment, written in 1925, after Lawrence had almost died from malaria. The leading character in the story, Gethin Day, is in a similar position. Weak from the effects of the fever, he is on his way back to England after many years abroad. On the voyage, he undergoes a transcendental experience: the victory of discovery after an interminable search; the piercing insight of the pure and lovely 'Greater Day', as opposed to ordinary and tedious 'little day'. Gethin Day sees the perfection of truth in the porpoises which swim alongside the ship, and so he continues his journey home with a newly awakened consciousness of the joy of life:

Gethin Day watched spell-bound, minute after minute, an hour, two hours, and still it was the same, the ship speeding, cutting the water, and the strong-bodied fish heading in perfect balance of speed underneath, mingling among themselves in some strange single laughter of multiple consciousness, giving off the joy of life, sheer joy of life, togetherness in pure complete motion, many lusty-bodied fish enjoying one laugh of life, sheer togetherness, perfect as passion. They gave off into the water their marvellous joy of life, such as the man had never met before. And it left him wonderstruck . . . he was mesmerized by one thing only, by joy, by joy of life, fish speeding in water with playful joy.

Here in lyrical and poetic prose Lawrence presents his vision of the lesson that mankind can learn from nature, 'the purest achievement of joy', the sheer joy that men have lost or never accomplished: 'No wonder Ocean was still mysterious, when such red hearts beat in it! No wonder man, with his tragedy, was a pale and sickly thing in comparison! What civilization will bring us to such a pitch of swift laughing togetherness, as these fish have reached?'

D. H. Lawrence had only a relatively short life, but he undoubtedly lived it to the full, producing a wide and varied body of work. Lawrence's legacy cannot be overstated. Although it is 70 years since his death, his novels, short stories and other writings remain unfailingly popular, which suggests that he will undoubtedly remain a significant literary figure in the twenty-first century.

Chronology

D. H. Lawrence's Life

1885 David Herbert Lawrence born in Eastwood, Nottinghamshire.

1898 Lawrence starts at Nottingham High School.

1901 Lawrence leaves school, meets Jessie Chambers, begins work in Nottingham as a clerk at J. H. Haywood, surgical-appliance manufacturer.

1902 Lawrence becomes a pupil-teacher at the British School in Eastwood.

1904 He spends time at a pupil-teacher centre in Ilkeston, Derbyshire.

1906 He becomes a student at University College, Nottingham.

1908 Lawrence moves to Croydon to teach at Davidson Road School.

1910 His mother, Lydia, dies.

1911 He suffers a serious illness. *The White Peacock*, his first novel, is published. 'Odour of Chrysanthemums' is published in the *English Review*.

1912 Lawrence meets Frieda Weekley. They leave together for Germany.

1913 *Sons and Lovers* and 'Her Turn' are published.

1914 Frieda is divorced, she marries Lawrence at Kensington Register Office, London.

1915 *The Rainbow* is published and then banned. The Lawrences move to Cornwall.

D. H. Lawrence's Times

1889   London dock strike.

1899   Start of the Boer War.
1901   Death of Queen Victoria. She is succeeded by Edward VII.

1902   Boer War ends.

1905   Einstein's Special Theory of Relativity published.

1908   Ford Madox Hueffer founds the *English Review*.

1910   Edward VII dies and is succeeded by George V.
1911   Coronation of George V. London dockers' and railworkers' strike. Suffragette riots in Whitehall, London.

1912   Coal miners', dockers' and transport workers' strike. The *Titanic* disaster.

1914   The start of the First World War. The Panama Canal is opened.
1915   Widespread use of trench warfare. Allied landings in Gallipoli. Einstein's General Theory of Relativity. The *Lusitania* is sunk.

1916   He begins *Women in Love*.

1919   The Lawrences leave England for Italy.
1920   They move to Taormina, Sicily.

1922   The Lawrences visit Ceylon (now Sri Lanka) and Australia. They go to New Mexico and settle at the Del Monte Ranch, near Taos. 'You Touched Me' is published in *England, My England* in New York. *The Fox* is published in the American magazine *The Dial*, in four instalments.
1923   They settle in Chapala, Mexico. Frieda returns to England in August, with Lawrence following in December. First British publication of *The Fox*.
1924   They return to Mexico and New Mexico. Lawrence's father dies. 'You Touched Me' is published in *England, My England* in England.
1925   Lawrence almost dies of malaria. He writes 'The Flying Fish' but does not finish it. The Lawrences return to Europe.
1926   They move to Florence, Italy. Lawrence takes up painting seriously.
1928   They move to Switzerland. *Lady Chatterley's Lover* is published.

1930   Lawrence dies of tuberculosis and is buried in Vence, France.
1935   Lawrence's body is exhumed and cremated, and the ashes are taken to Taos.
1936   'The Flying Fish' is published.

1916   Easter Monday uprising in Dublin. Conscription is introduced in the UK. Daylight saving is introduced in the UK. Severe food rationing in Germany.

1917   October Revolution in Russia. Freud publishes *Introduction to Psychoanalysis*.

1918   End of the First World War. Armistice signed on 11 November. The vote is granted to women over the age of 30 in the UK. Severe world-wide influenza epidemic.

1919   German National Socialist (Nazi) Party founded. Irish Free State declared. Mussolini founds the Fascist Party in Italy. The first direct aeroplane crossing of the Atlantic.

1921   Miners' strike in UK. State of Emergency declared in Germany. Einstein wins the Nobel Prize for Physics.

1922   Creation of the USSR. Fascists form a government in Italy. British Broadcasting Corporation is established.

1923   London dock strike. Riots in Germany.

1924   First Labour government in the UK.

1926   General Strike in the UK. Television invented by John Logie Baird.

1928   Women able to vote at 21 in the UK. Alexander Fleming discovers penicillin.

1929   Collapse of the New York Stock Exchange.

The Fox and Other Stories

Her Turn

She was his second wife, and so there was between them that truce 🎧
which is never held between a man and his first woman.

He was one for the women, and as such, an exception among
the colliers. In spite of their prudery, the neighbour women liked
him; he was big, naïve, and very courteous with them; he was so,   5
even to his second wife.

Being a large man of considerable strength and perfect health,
he earned good money in the pit. His natural courtesy saved him
from enemies, while his fresh interest in life made his presence
always agreeable. So he went his own way, had always plenty of   10
friends, always a good job down pit.

He gave his wife thirty-five shillings a week. He had two
grown-up sons at home, and they paid twelve shillings each. There
was only one child by the second marriage, so Radford considered
his wife did well.   15

Eighteen months ago, Bryan and Wentworth's men were out on
strike for eleven weeks. During that time, Mrs Radford could
neither cajole nor entreat nor nag the ten shillings strike-pay from
her husband. So that when the second strike came on, she was
prepared for action.   20

Radford was going, quite inconspicuously, to the publican's wife
at the 'Golden Horn'. She is a large, easy-going lady of forty, and
her husband is sixty-three, moreover crippled with rheumatism.
She sits in the little bar-parlour of the wayside public-house, knit-
ting for dear life, and sipping a very moderate glass of Scotch.   25
When a decent man arrives at the three-foot width of bar, she rises,
serves him, surveys him over, and, if she likes his looks, says:

3

'Won't you step inside sir?'

If he steps inside, he will find not more than one or two men present. The room is warm, quite small. The landlady knits. She gives a few polite words to the stranger, then resumes her conver-
5 sation with the man who interests her most. She is straight, highly-coloured, with indifferent brown eyes.

'What was that you asked me, Mr Radford?'

'What is the difference between a donkey's tail and a rainbow?' asked Radford, who had a consuming passion for conundrums.

10 'All the difference in the world,' replied the landlady.

'Yes, but what special difference?'

'I s'll have to give it up again. You'll think me a donkey's head, I'm afraid.'

'Not likely. But just you consider now, wheer . . .'

15 The conundrum was still under weigh, when a girl entered. She was swarthy, a fine animal. After she had gone out:

'Do you know who that is?' asked the landlady.

'I can't say as I do,' replied Radford.

'She's Frederick Pinnock's daughter, from Stony Ford. She's
20 courting our Willy.'

'And a fine lass, too.'

'Yes, fine enough, as far as that goes. What sort of a wife'll she make him, think you?'

'You just let me consider a bit,' said the man. He took out a
25 pocket-book and a pencil. The landlady continued to talk to the other guests.

Radford was a big fellow, black-haired, with a brown moustache, and darkish blue eyes. His voice, naturally deep, was pitched in his throat, and had a peculiar, tenor quality, rather husky, and
30 disturbing. He modulated it a good deal as he spoke, as men do who talk much with women. Always, there was a certain indolence in his carriage.

'Our mester's lazy,' his wife said. 'There's many a bit of a job wants doin', but get him to do it if you can.'

35 But she knew he was merely indifferent to the little jobs, and not lazy.

He sat writing for about ten minutes, at the end of which time, he read:

'I see a fine girl full of life.

I see her just ready for wedlock,

But there's jealousy between her eyebrows

And jealousy on her mouth.

I see trouble ahead.

Willy is delicate.

She would do him no good.

She would never see when he wasn't well,

She would only see what she wanted –'

So, in phrases, he got down his thoughts. He had to fumble for expression, and therefore anything serious he wanted to say he wrote in 'poetry', as he called it.

Presently, the landlady rose, saying:

'Well, I s'll have to be looking after our mester. I s'll be in again before we close.'

Radford sat quite comfortably on. In a while, he too bade the company good night.

When he got home, at a quarter-past eleven, his sons were in bed, and his wife sat awaiting him. She was a woman of medium height, fat and sleek, a dumpling. Her black hair was parted smooth, her narrow-opened eyes were sly and satirical, she had a peculiar twang in her rather sleering voice.

'Our missis is a puss-puss,' he said easily, of her. Her extraordinarily smooth, sleek face was remarkable. She was very healthy.

He never came in drunk. Having taken off his coat and his cap, he sat down to supper in his shirt-sleeves. Do as he might, she was fascinated by him. He had a strong neck, with the crisp hair growing low. Let her be angry as she would, yet she had a passion for that neck of his, particularly when she saw the great vein rib under the skin.

'I think, Missis,' he said, 'I'd rather ha'e a smite o' cheese than this meat.'

'Well, can't you get it yourself?'

'Yi, surely I can,' he said, and went out to the pantry.

'I think, if yer comin' in at this time of night, you can wait on yourself,' she justified herself.

5 She moved uneasily in her chair. There were several jam-tarts alongside the cheese on the dish he brought.

'Yi, Missis, them tan-tafflins'll go down very nicely,' he said.

'Oh, will they! Then you'd better help to pay for them,' she said, amiably, but determined.

'Now what art after?'

10 'What am I after? Why, can't you think?' she said sarcastically.

'I'm not for thinkin', Missis.'

'No, I know you're not. But wheer's my money? You've been paid the Union today. Wheer do I come in?'

'Tha's got money, an' tha mun use it.'

15 'Thank yer. An' 'aven't you none, as well?'

'I hadna, not till we was paid, not a ha'p'ny.'

'Then you ought to be ashamed of yourself to say so.'

''Appen so.'

'We'll go shares wi' th' Union money,' she said. 'That's nothing 20 but what's right.'

'We shonna. Tha's got plenty o' money as tha can use.'

'Oh, all right,' she said. 'I will do.'

She went to bed. It made her feel sharp that she could not get at him.

25 The next day, she was just as usual. But at eleven o'clock she took her purse and went up town. Trade was very slack. Men stood about in gangs, men were playing marbles everywhere in the streets. It was a sunny morning. Mrs Radford went into the furnisher-and-upholsterer's shop.

30 'There's a few things,' she said to Mr Allcock, 'as I'm wantin' for the house, and I might as well get them now, while the men's at home, and can shift me the furniture.'

She put her fat purse on to the counter with a click. The man should know she was not wanting 'strap'. She bought linoleum for 35 the kitchen, a new wringer, a breakfast-service, a spring mattress, and various other things, keeping a mere thirty shillings, which she tied in a corner of her handkerchief. In her purse was some loose silver.

Her husband was gardening in a desultory fashion when she got back home. The daffodils were out. The colts in the field at the end of the garden were tossing their velvety brown necks.

'Sithee here, Missis,' called Radford, from the shed which stood half-way down the path. Two doves in a cage were cooing.

'What have you got?' asked the woman, as she approached. He held out to her in his big, earthy hand, a tortoise. The reptile was very, very slowly issuing its head again to the warmth.

'He's wakened up betimes,' said Radford.

'He's like th' men, wakened up for a holiday,' said the wife. Radford scratched the little beast's scaly head.

'We pleased to see him out,' he said.

They had just finished dinner, when a man knocked at the door.

'From Allcock's!' he said.

The plump woman took up the clothes-basket containing the crockery she had bought.

'Whativer hast got theer?' asked her husband.

'We've been wantin' some breakfast-cups for ages, so I went up town an' got 'em this mornin',' she replied.

He watched her taking out the crockery.

'Hm!' he said. 'Tha's been on th' spend, seemly.'

Again there was a thud at the door. The man had put down a roll of linoleum. Mr Radford went to look at it.

'They come rolling in!' he exclaimed.

'Who's grumbled more than you about the raggy oilcloth of this kitchen?' said the insidious, cat-like voice of the wife.

'It's all right, it's all right,' said Radford.

The carter came up the entry with another roll, which he deposited with a grunt at the door.

'An' how much do you reckon this lot is?' he asked.

'Oh, they're all paid for, don't worry,' replied the wife.

'Shall yer gi'e me a hand, Mester?' asked the carter.

Radford followed him down the entry, in his easy, slouching way. His wife went after. His waistcoat was hanging loose over his shirt. She watched his easy movement of well-being as she followed him, and she laughed to herself.

The carter took hold of one end of the wire mattress, dragged it forth.

5 'Well, this is a corker!' said Radford, as he received the burden.

'Now the mangle!' said the carter.

'What dost reckon tha's been up to, Missis?' asked the husband.

'I said to myself last wash-day, if I had to turn that mangle again, tha'd ha'e ter wash the clothes thyself.'

10 Radford followed the carter down the entry again. In the street, women were standing watching, and dozens of men were lounging round the cart. One officiously helped with the wringer.

'Gi'e him thrippence,' said Mrs Radford.

'Gi'e 't him thysen,' replied her husband.

15 'I've no change under half-a-crown.'

Radford tipped the carter, and returned indoors. He surveyed the array of crockery, linoleum, mattress, mangle, and other goods crowding the house and the yard.

'Well, this is a winder!' he repeated.

20 'We stood in need of 'em enough,' she replied.

'I hope tha's got plenty more from wheer they came from,' he replied dangerously.

'That's just what I haven't.' She opened her purse. 'Two half-crowns, that's every copper I've got i' th' world.'

25 He stood very still as he looked.

'It's right,' she said.

There was a certain smug sense of satisfaction about her. A wave of anger came over him, blinding him. But he waited and waited. Suddenly his arm leapt up, the fist clenched, and his eyes blazed

30 at her. She shrank away, pale and frightened. But he dropped his fist to his side, turned, and went out, muttering. He went down to the shed that stood in the middle of the garden. There he picked up the tortoise, and stood with bent head, rubbing its horny head.

She stood hesitating, watching him. Her heart was heavy, and

35 yet there was a curious, cat-like look of satisfaction round her eyes. Then she went indoors and gazed at her new cups, admiringly.

The next week he handed her his half-sovereign without a word.

'You'll want some for yourself,' she said, and she gave him a shilling. He accepted it.

Odour of Chrysanthemums

I

The small locomotive engine, Number 4, came clanking, stumbling down from Selston with seven full waggons. It appeared round the corner with loud threats of speed, but the colt that it startled from among the gorse, which still flickered indistinctly in the raw
5 afternoon, outdistanced it at a canter. A woman, walking up the railway line to Underwood, drew back into the hedge, held her basket aside, and watched the footplate of the engine advancing. The trucks thumped heavily past, one by one, with slow inevitable movement, as she stood insignificantly trapped between the jolting
10 black waggons and the hedge; then they curved away towards the coppice where the withered oak leaves dropped noiselessly, while the birds, pulling at the scarlet hips beside the track, made off into the dusk that had already crept into the spinney. In the open, the smoke from the engine sank and cleaved to the rough grass. The
15 fields were dreary and forsaken, and in the marshy strip that led to the whimsey, a reedy pit-pond, the fowls had already abandoned their run among the alders, to roost in the tarred fowl-house. The pit-bank loomed up beyond the pond, flames like red sores licking its ashy sides, in the afternoon's stagnant light. Just beyond rose
20 the tapering chimneys and the clumsy black headstocks of Brinsley Colliery. The two wheels were spinning fast up against the sky, and the winding-engine rapped out its little spasms. The miners were being turned up.

    The engine whistled as it came into the wide bay of railway lines
25 beside the colliery, where rows of trucks stood in harbour.

Miners, single, trailing and in groups, passed like shadows diverging home. At the edge of the ribbed level of sidings squat a low cottage, three steps down from the cinder track. A large bony vine clutched at the house, as if to claw down the tiled roof. Round the bricked yard grew a few wintry primroses. Beyond, the long garden sloped down to a bush-covered brook course. There were some twiggy apple trees, winter-crack trees, and ragged cabbages. Beside the path hung dishevelled pink chrysanthemums, like pink cloths hung on bushes. A woman came stooping out of the felt-covered fowl-house, half-way down the garden. She closed and padlocked the door, then drew herself erect, having brushed some bits from her white apron.

She was a tall woman of imperious mien, handsome, with definite black eyebrows. Her smooth black hair was parted exactly. For a few moments she stood steadily watching the miners as they passed along the railway: then she turned towards the brook course. Her face was calm and set, her mouth was closed with disillusionment. After a moment she called:

'John!' There was no answer. She waited, and then said distinctly:

'Where are you?'

'Here!' replied a child's sulky voice from among the bushes. The woman looked piercingly through the dusk.

'Are you at that brook?' she asked sternly.

For answer the child showed himself before the raspberry-canes that rose like whips. He was a small, sturdy boy of five. He stood quite still, defiantly.

'Oh!' said the mother, conciliated. 'I thought you were down at that wet brook – and you remember what I told you –'

The boy did not move or answer.

'Come, come on in,' she said more gently, 'it's getting dark. There's your grandfather's engine coming down the line!'

The lad advanced slowly, with resentful, taciturn movement. He was dressed in trousers and waistcoat of cloth that was too thick and hard for the size of the garments. They were evidently cut down from a man's clothes.

As they went slowly towards the house he tore at the ragged wisps of chrysanthemums and dropped the petals in handfuls along the path.

'Don't do that – it does look nasty,' said his mother. He refrained, and she, suddenly pitiful, broke off a twig with three or four wan flowers and held them against her face. When mother and son reached the yard her hand hesitated, and instead of laying the flower aside, she pushed it in her apron-band. The mother and son stood at the foot of the three steps looking across the bay of lines at the passing home of the miners. The trundle of the small train was imminent. Suddenly the engine loomed past the house and came to a stop opposite the gate.

The engine-driver, a short man with a round grey beard, leaned out of the cab high above the woman.

'Have you got a cup of tea?' he said in a cheery, hearty fashion.

It was her father. She went in, saying she would mash. Directly, she returned.

'I didn't come to see you on Sunday,' began the little grey-bearded man.

'I didn't expect you,' said his daughter.

The engine-driver winced; then, reassuming his cheery, airy manner, he said:

'Oh, have you heard then? Well, and what do you think –?'

'I think it is soon enough,' she replied.

At her brief censure the little man made an impatient gesture, and said coaxingly, yet with dangerous coldness:

'Well, what's a man to do? It's no sort of life for a man of my years, to sit at my own hearth like a stranger. And if I'm going to marry again it may as well be soon as late – what does it matter to anybody?'

The woman did not reply, but turned and went into the house. The man in the engine-cab stood assertive, till she returned with a cup of tea and a piece of bread and butter on a plate. She went up the steps and stood near the footplate of the hissing engine.

'You needn't 'a' brought me bread an' butter,' said her father. 'But a cup of tea' – he sipped appreciatively – 'it's very nice.' He sipped for a moment or two, then: 'I hear as Walter's got another bout on,' he said.

'When hasn't he?' said the woman bitterly.

'I heered tell of him in the "Lord Nelson" braggin' as he was going to spend that b— afore he went: half a sovereign that was.' 5

'When?' asked the woman.

'A' Sat'day night – I know that's true.'

'Very likely,' she laughed bitterly. 'He gives me twenty-three shillings.'

'Aye, it's a nice thing, when a man can do nothing with his 10 money but make a beast of himself!' said the grey-whiskered man. The woman turned her head away. Her father swallowed the last of his tea and handed her the cup.

'Aye,' he sighed, wiping his mouth. 'It's a settler, it is –'

He put his hand on the lever. The little engine strained and 15 groaned, and the train rumbled towards the crossing. The woman again looked across the metals. Darkness was settling over the spaces of the railway and trucks: the miners, in grey sombre groups, were still passing home. The winding-engine pulsed hurriedly, with brief pauses. Elizabeth Bates looked at the dreary flow of men, 20 then she went indoors. Her husband did not come.

The kitchen was small and full of firelight; red coals piled glowing up the chimney mouth. All the life of the room seemed in the white, warm hearth and the steel fender reflecting the red fire. The cloth was laid for tea; cups glinted in the shadows. At the back, 25 where the lowest stairs protruded into the room, the boy sat struggling with a knife and a piece of whitewood. He was almost hidden in the shadow. It was half-past four. They had but to await the father's coming to begin tea. As the mother watched her son's sullen little struggle with the wood, she saw herself in his silence 30 and pertinacity; she saw the father in her child's indifference to all but himself. She seemed to be occupied by her husband. He had probably gone past his home, slunk past his own door, to drink before he came in, while his dinner spoiled and wasted in waiting. She glanced at the clock, then took the potatoes to strain them in 35 the yard. The garden and fields beyond the brook were closed in uncertain darkness. When she rose with the saucepan, leaving the drain steaming into the night behind her, she saw the yellow lamps were lit along the high road that went up the hill away beyond the space of the railway lines and the field.

5 Then again she watched the men trooping home, fewer now and fewer.

Indoors the fire was sinking and the room was dark red. The woman put her saucepan on the hob, and set a batter pudding near the mouth of the oven. Then she stood unmoving. Directly, 10 gratefully, came quick young steps to the door. Someone hung on the latch a moment, then a little girl entered and began pulling off her outdoor things, dragging a mass of curls, just ripening from gold to brown, over her eyes with her hat.

Her mother chid her for coming late from school, and said she 15 would have to keep her at home the dark winter days.

'Why, mother, it's hardly a bit dark yet. The lamp's not lighted, and my father's not home.'

'No, he isn't. But it's a quarter to five! Did you see anything of him?'

20 The child became serious. She looked at her mother with large, wistful blue eyes.

'No, mother, I've never seen him. Why? Has he come up an' gone past, to Old Brinsley? He hasn't, mother, 'cos I never saw him.'

'He'd watch that,' said the mother bitterly, 'he'd take care as 25 you didn't see him. But you may depend upon it, he's seated in the "Prince o' Wales". He wouldn't be this late.'

The girl looked at her mother piteously.

'Let's have our teas, mother, should we?' said she.

The mother called John to table. She opened the door once more 30 and looked out across the darkness of the lines. All was deserted: she could not hear the winding-engines.

'Perhaps,' she said to herself, 'he's stopped to get some ripping done.'

They sat down to tea. John, at the end of the table near the door, 35 was almost lost in the darkness. Their faces were hidden from each other. The girl crouched against the fender slowly moving a thick piece of bread before the fire. The lad, his face a dusky mark on the shadow, sat watching her who was transfigured in the red glow.

'I do think it's beautiful to look in the fire,' said the child.

'Do you?' said her mother. 'Why?'

'It's so red, and full of little caves – and it feels so nice, and you can fair smell it.'

'It'll want mending directly,' replied her mother, 'and then if your father comes he'll carry on and say there never is a fire when a man comes home sweating from the pit. – A public-house is always warm enough.'

There was silence till the boy said complainingly: 'Make haste, our Annie.'

'Well, I am doing! I can't make the fire do it no faster, can I?'

'She keeps wafflin' it about so's to make 'er slow,' grumbled the boy.

'Don't have such an evil imagination, child,' replied the mother.

Soon the room was busy in the darkness with the crisp sound of crunching. The mother ate very little. She drank her tea determinedly, and sat thinking. When she rose her anger was evident in the stern unbending of her head. She looked at the pudding in the fender, and broke out:

'It is a scandalous thing as a man can't even come home to his dinner! If it's crozzled up to a cinder I don't see why I should care. Past his very door he goes to get to a public-house, and here I sit with his dinner waiting for him –'

She went out. As she dropped piece after piece of coal on the red fire, the shadows fell on the walls, till the room was almost in total darkness.

'I canna see,' grumbled the invisible John. In spite of herself, the mother laughed.

'You know the way to your mouth,' she said. She set the dustpan outside the door. When she came again like a shadow on the hearth, the lad repeated, complaining sulkily:

'I canna see.'

'Good gracious!' cried the mother irritably, 'you're as bad as your father if it's a bit dusk!'

Nevertheless she took a paper spill from a sheaf on the mantelpiece and proceeded to light the lamp that hung from the ceiling in the middle of the room. As she reached up, her figure displayed itself just rounding with maternity.

5 'Oh, mother –!' exclaimed the girl.

'What?' said the woman, suspended in the act of putting the lamp glass over the flame. The copper reflector shone handsomely on her, as she stood with uplifted arm, turning to face her daughter.

'You've got a flower in your apron!' said the child, in a little 10 rapture at this unusual event.

'Goodness me!' exclaimed the woman, relieved. 'One would think the house was afire.' She replaced the glass and waited a moment before turning up the wick. A pale shadow was seen floating vaguely on the floor.

15 'Let me smell!' said the child, still rapturously, coming forward and putting her face to her mother's waist.

'Go along, silly!' said the mother, turning up the lamp. The light revealed their suspense so that the woman felt it almost unbearable. Annie was still bending at her waist. Irritably, the mother took the 20 flowers out from her apron-band.

'Oh, mother – don't take them out!' Annie cried, catching her hand and trying to replace the sprig.

'Such nonsense!' said the mother, turning away. The child put the pale chrysanthemums to her lips, murmuring:

25 'Don't they smell beautiful!'

Her mother gave a short laugh.

'No,' she said, 'not to me. It was chrysanthemums when I married him, and chrysanthemums when you were born, and the first time they ever brought him home drunk, he'd got brown 30 chrysanthemums in his button-hole.'

She looked at the children. Their eyes and their parted lips were wondering. The mother sat rocking in silence for some time. Then she looked at the clock.

'Twenty minutes to six!' In a tone of fine bitter carelessness she 35 continued: 'Eh, he'll not come now till they bring him. There he'll stick! But he needn't come rolling in here in his pit-dirt, for *I* won't wash him. He can lie on the floor – Eh, what a fool I've been, what a fool! And this is what I came here for, to this dirty hole, rats and all, for him to slink past his very door. Twice last week – he's begun now –'

She silenced herself, and rose to clear the table.

While for an hour or more the children played, subduedly intent, fertile of imagination, united in fear of the mother's wrath, and in dread of their father's home-coming, Mrs Bates sat in her rocking-chair making a 'singlet' of thick cream-coloured flannel, which gave a dull wounded sound as she tore off the grey edge. She worked at her sewing with energy, listening to the children, and her anger wearied itself, lay down to rest, opening its eyes from time to time and steadily watching, its ears raised to listen. Sometimes even her anger quailed and shrank, and the mother suspended her sewing, tracing the footsteps that thudded along the sleepers outside; she would lift her head sharply to bid the children 'hush', but she recovered herself in time, and the footsteps went past the gate, and the children were not flung out of their playing world.

But at last Annie sighed, and gave in. She glanced at her waggon of slippers, and loathed the game. She turned plaintively to her mother.

'Mother!' – but she was inarticulate.

John crept out like a frog from under the sofa. His mother glanced up.

'Yes,' she said, 'just look at those shirt-sleeves!'

The boy held them out to survey them, saying nothing. Then somebody called in a hoarse voice away down the line, and suspense bristled in the room, till two people had gone by outside, talking.

'It is time for bed,' said the mother.

'My father hasn't come,' wailed Annie plaintively. But her mother was primed with courage.

'Never mind. They'll bring him when he does come – like a log.' She meant there would be no scene. 'And he may sleep on the floor till he wakes himself. I know he'll not go to work tomorrow after this!'

The children had their hands and faces wiped with a flannel.

They were very quiet. When they had put on their nightdresses, they said their prayers, the boy mumbling. The mother looked down at them, at the brown silken bush of intertwining curls in the nape of the girl's neck, at the little black head of the lad, and her
5 heart burst with anger at their father who caused all three such distress. The children hid their faces in her skirts for comfort.

When Mrs Bates came down, the room was strangely empty, with a tension of expectancy. She took up her sewing and stitched for some time without raising her head. Meantime her anger was
10 tinged with fear.

II

The clock struck eight and she rose suddenly, dropping her sewing on her chair. She went to the stairfoot door, opened it, listening. Then she went out, locking the door behind her.

Something scuffled in the yard, and she started, though she knew
15 it was only the rats with which the place was overrun. The night was very dark. In the great bay of railway lines, bulked with trucks, there was no trace of light, only away back she could see a few yellow lamps at the pit-top, and the red smear of the burning pit-bank on the night. She hurried along the edge of the track, then, crossing the converging
20 lines, came to the stile by the white gates, whence she emerged on the road. Then the fear which had led her shrank. People were walking up to New Brinsley; she saw the lights in the houses; twenty yards further on were the broad windows of the 'Prince of Wales', very warm and bright, and the loud voices of men could
25 be heard distinctly. What a fool she had been to imagine that anything had happened to him! He was merely drinking over there at the 'Prince of Wales'. She faltered. She had never yet been to fetch him, and she never would go. So she continued her walk towards the long straggling line of houses, standing blank on the
30 highway. She entered a passage between the dwellings.

'Mr Rigley? – Yes! Did you want him? No, he's not in at this minute.'

The raw-boned woman leaned forward from her dark scullery and peered at the other, upon whom fell a dim light through the blind of the kitchen window.

'Is it Mrs Bates?' she asked in a tone tinged with respect.

'Yes. I wondered if your Master was at home. Mine hasn't come yet.'

''Asn't 'e! Oh, Jack's been 'ome an' 'ad 'is dinner an' gone out. 'E's just gone for 'alf an hour afore bedtime. Did you call at the "Prince of Wales"?'

'No –'

'No, you didn't like – ! It's not very nice.' The other woman was indulgent. There was an awkward pause. 'Jack never said nothink about – about your Mester,' she said.

'No! – I expect he's stuck in there!'

Elizabeth Bates said this bitterly, and with recklessness. She knew that the woman across the yard was standing at her door listening, but she did not care. As she turned:

'Stop a minute! I'll just go an' ask Jack if 'e knows anythink,' said Mrs Rigley.

'Oh, no – I wouldn't like to put –!'

'Yes, I will, if you'll just step inside an' see as th' childer doesn't come downstairs and set theirselves afire.'

Elizabeth Bates, murmuring a remonstrance, stepped inside. The other woman apologized for the state of the room.

The kitchen needed apology. There were little frocks and trousers and childish undergarments on the squab and on the floor, and a litter of playthings everywhere. On the black American cloth of the table were pieces of bread and cake, crusts, slops, and a teapot with cold tea.

'Eh, ours is just as bad,' said Elizabeth Bates, looking at the woman, not at the house. Mrs Rigley put a shawl over her head and hurried out, saying:

'I shanna be a minute.'

The other sat, noting with faint disapproval the general untidiness of the room. Then she fell to counting the shoes of various sizes scattered over the floor. There were twelve. She sighed

and said to herself, 'No wonder!' – glancing at the litter. There came the scratching of two pairs of feet on the yard, and the Rigleys entered. Elizabeth Bates rose. Rigley was a big man, with very large bones. His head looked particularly bony. Across his temple was a
5 blue scar, caused by a wound got in the pit, a wound in which the coal-dust remained blue like tattooing.

''Asna 'e come whoam yit?' asked the man, without any form of greeting, but with deference and sympathy. 'I couldna say wheer he is – 'e's non ower theer!' – he jerked his head to signify the
10 'Prince of Wales'.

''E's 'appen gone up to th' "Yew",' said Mrs Rigley.

There was another pause. Rigley had evidently something to get off his mind:

'Ah left 'im finishin' a stint,' he began. 'Loose-all 'ad bin gone
15 about ten minutes when we com'n away, an' I shouted, "Are ter comin', Walt?" an' 'e said, "Go on, Ah shanna be but a'ef a minnit," so we com'n ter th' bottom, me an' Bowers, thinkin' as 'e wor just behint, an' 'ud come up i' th' next bantle –'

He stood perplexed, as if answering a charge of deserting his
20 mate. Elizabeth Bates, now again certain of disaster, hastened to reassure him:

'I expect 'e's gone up to th' "Yew Tree", as you say. It's not the first time. I've fretted myself into a fever before now. He'll come home when they carry him.'

25 'Ay, isn't it too bad!' deplored the other woman.

'I'll just step up to Dick's an' see if 'e *is* theer,' offered the man, afraid of appearing alarmed, afraid of taking liberties.

'Oh, I wouldn't think of bothering you that far,' said Elizabeth Bates, with emphasis, but he knew she was glad of his offer.

30 As they stumbled up the entry, Elizabeth Bates heard Rigley's wife run across the yard and open her neighbour's door. At this, suddenly all the blood in her body seemed to switch away from her heart.

'Mind!' warned Rigley. 'Ah've said many a time as Ah'd fill up
35 them ruts in this entry, sumb'dy 'll be breakin' their legs yit.'

She recovered herself and walked quickly along with the miner.

'I don't like leaving the children in bed, and nobody in the house,' she said.

'No, you dunna!' he replied courteously. They were soon at the gate of the cottage.

'Well, I shanna be many minnits. Dunna you be frettin' now, 'e'll be all right,' said the butty.

'Thank you very much, Mr Rigley,' she replied.

'You're welcome!' he stammered, moving away. 'I shanna be many minnits.'

The house was quiet. Elizabeth Bates took off her hat and shawl, and rolled back the rug. When she had finished, she sat down. It was a few minutes past nine. She was startled by the rapid chuff of the winding-engine at the pit, and the sharp whirr of the brakes on the rope as it descended. Again she felt the painful sweep of her blood, and she put her hand to her side, saying aloud, 'Good gracious! – it's only the nine o'clock deputy going down,' rebuking herself.

She sat still, listening. Half an hour of this, and she was wearied out.

'What am I working myself up like this for?' she said pitiably to herself, 'I s'll only be doing myself some damage.'

She took out her sewing again.

At a quarter to ten there were footsteps. One person! She watched for the door to open. It was an elderly woman, in a black bonnet and a black woollen shawl – his mother. She was about sixty years old, pale, with blue eyes, and her face all wrinkled and lamentable. She shut the door and turned to her daughter-in-law peevishly.

'Eh, Lizzie, whatever shall we do, whatever shall we do!' she cried.

Elizabeth drew back a little, sharply.

'What is it, mother?' she said.

The elder woman seated herself on the sofa.

'I don't know, child, I can't tell you!' – she shook her head slowly. Elizabeth sat watching her, anxious and vexed.

'I don't know,' replied the grandmother, sighing very deeply. 'There's no end to my troubles, there isn't. The things I've gone through, I'm sure it's enough –!' She wept without wiping her eyes, the tears running.

'But, mother,' interrupted Elizabeth, 'what do you mean? What is it?'

5   The grandmother slowly wiped her eyes. The fountains of her tears were stopped by Elizabeth's directness. She wiped her eyes slowly.

'Poor child! Eh, you poor thing!' she moaned. 'I don't know what we're going to do, I don't – and you as you are – it's a thing, it is indeed!'

10   Elizabeth waited.

'Is he dead?' she asked, and at the words her heart swung violently, though she felt a slight flush of shame at the ultimate extravagance of the question. Her words sufficiently frightened the old lady, almost brought her to herself.

15   'Don't say so, Elizabeth! We'll hope it's not as bad as that; no, may the Lord spare us that, Elizabeth. Jack Rigley came just as I was sittin' down to a glass afore going to bed, an' 'e said, "'Appen you'll go down th' line, Mrs Bates. Walt's had an accident. 'Appen you'll go an' sit wi' 'er till we can get him home." I hadn't time to
20 ask him a word afore he was gone. An' I put my bonnet on an' come straight down, Lizzie. I thought to myself, "Eh, that poor blessed child, if anybody should come an' tell her of a sudden, there's no knowin' what'll 'appen to 'er." You mustn't let it upset you, Lizzie – or you know what to expect. How long is it, six
25 months – or is it five, Lizzie? Ay!' – the old woman shook her head – 'time slips on, it slips on! Ay!'

Elizabeth's thoughts were busy elsewhere. If he was killed – would she be able to manage on the little pension and what she could earn? – she counted up rapidly. If he was hurt – they wouldn't
30 take him to the hospital – how tiresome he would be to nurse! – but perhaps she'd be able to get him away from the drink and his hateful ways. She would – while he was ill. The tears offered to come to her eyes at the picture. But what sentimental luxury was this she was beginning? – She turned to consider the children. At
35 any rate she was absolutely necessary for them. They were her business.

'Ay!' repeated the old woman, 'it seems but a week or two since he brought me his first wages. Ay – he was a good lad, Elizabeth, he was, in his way. I don't know why he got to be such a trouble, I don't. He was a happy lad at home, only full of spirits. But there's no mistake he's been a handful of trouble, he has! I hope the Lord'll spare him to mend his ways. I hope so, I hope so. You've had a sight o' trouble with him, Elizabeth, you have indeed. But he was a jolly enough lad wi' me, he was, I can assure you. I don't know how it is . . .'

The old woman continued to muse aloud, a monotonous irritating sound, while Elizabeth thought concentratedly, startled once, when she heard the winding-engine chuff quickly, and the brakes skirr with a shriek. Then she heard the engine more slowly, and the brakes made no sound. The old woman did not notice. Elizabeth waited in suspense. The mother-in-law talked, with lapses into silence.

'But he wasn't your son, Lizzie, an' it makes a difference. Whatever he was, I remember him when he was little, an' I learned to understand him and to make allowances. You've got to make allowances for them –'

It was half-past ten, and the old woman was saying: 'But it's trouble from beginning to end; you're never too old for trouble, never too old for that –' when the gate banged back, and there were heavy feet on the steps.

'I'll go, Lizzie, let me go,' cried the old woman, rising. But Elizabeth was at the door. It was a man in pit-clothes.

'They're bringin' 'im, Missis,' he said. Elizabeth's heart halted a moment. Then it surged on again, almost suffocating her.

'Is he – is it bad?' she asked.

The man turned away, looking at the darkness:

'The doctor says 'e'd been dead hours. 'E saw 'im i' th' lamp-cabin.'

The old woman, who stood just behind Elizabeth, dropped into a chair, and folded her hands, crying: 'Oh, my boy, my boy!'

'Hush!' said Elizabeth, with a sharp twitch of a frown. 'Be still, mother, don't waken th' children: I wouldn't have them down for anything!'

The old woman moaned softly, rocking herself. The man was drawing away. Elizabeth took a step forward.

'How was it?' she asked.

'Well, I couldn't say for sure,' the man replied, very ill at ease.
'E wor finishin' a stint an' th' butties 'ad gone, an' a lot o' stuff come down atop 'n 'im.'

'And crushed him?' cried the widow, with a shudder.

'No,' said the man, 'it fell at th' back of 'im. 'E wor under th' face, an' it niver touched 'im. It shut 'im in. It seems 'e wor smothered.'

Elizabeth shrank back. She heard the old woman behind her cry:
'What? – what did 'e say it was?'

The man replied, more loudly: ''E wor smothered!'

Then the old woman wailed aloud, and this relieved Elizabeth.

'Oh, mother,' she said, putting her hand on the old woman, 'don't waken th' children, don't waken th' children.'

She wept a little, unknowing, while the old mother rocked herself and moaned. Elizabeth remembered that they were bringing him home, and she must be ready. 'They'll lay him in the parlour,' she said to herself, standing a moment pale and perplexed.

Then she lighted a candle and went into the tiny room. The air was cold and damp, but she could not make a fire, there was no fire-place. She set down the candle and looked round. The candle-light glittered on the lustre-glasses, on the two vases that held some of the pink chrysanthemums, and on the dark mahogany. There was a cold, deathly smell of chrysanthemums in the room. Elizabeth stood looking at the flowers. She turned away, and calculated whether there would be room to lay him on the floor, between the couch and the chiffonier. She pushed the chairs aside. There would be room to lay him down and to step round him. Then she fetched the old red table-cloth, and another old cloth, spreading them down to save her bit of carpet. She shivered on leaving the parlour; so, from the dresser-drawer she took a clean shirt and put it at the fire to air. All the time her mother-in-law was rocking herself in the chair and moaning.

'You'll have to move from there, mother,' said Elizabeth. 'They'll be bringing him in. Come in the rocker.'

The old mother rose mechanically, and seated herself by the fire, continuing to lament. Elizabeth went into the pantry for another candle, and there, in the little penthouse under the naked tiles, she heard them coming. She stood still in the pantry doorway, listening. She heard them pass the end of the house, and come awkwardly down the three steps, a jumble of shuffling footsteps and muttering voices. The old woman was silent. The men were in the yard.

Then Elizabeth heard Matthews, the manager of the pit, say: 'You go in first, Jim. Mind!'

The door came open, and the two women saw a collier backing into the room, holding one end of a stretcher, on which they could see the nailed pit-boots of the dead man. The two carriers halted, the man at the head stooping to the lintel of the door.

'Wheer will you have him?' asked the manager, a short, white-bearded man.

Elizabeth roused herself and came from the pantry carrying the unlighted candle.

'In the parlour,' she said.

'In there, Jim!' pointed the manager, and the carriers backed round into the tiny room. The coat with which they had covered the body fell off as they awkwardly turned through the two doorways, and the women saw their man, naked to the waist, lying stripped for work. The old woman began to moan in a low voice of horror.

'Lay th' stretcher at th' side,' snapped the manager, 'an' put 'im on th' cloths. Mind now, mind! Look you now – !'

One of the men had knocked off a vase of chrysanthemums. He stared awkwardly, then they set down the stretcher. Elizabeth did not look at her husband. As soon as she could get in the room, she went and picked up the broken vase and the flowers.

'Wait a minute!' she said.

The three men waited in silence while she mopped up the water with a duster.

'Eh, what a job, what a job, to be sure!' the manager was saying, rubbing his brow with trouble and perplexity. 'Never knew such a thing in my life, never! He'd no business to ha' been left. I never knew such a thing in my life! Fell over him clean as a whistle, an' shut him in. Not four foot of space, there wasn't – yet it scarce bruised him.'

He looked down at the dead man, lying prone, half naked, all 5 grimed with coal-dust.

'"'Sphyxiated," the doctor said. It *is* the most terrible job I've ever known. Seems as if it was done o' purpose. Clean over him, an' shut 'im in, like a mouse-trap' – he made a sharp, descending gesture with his hand.

10 The colliers standing by jerked aside their heads in hopeless comment.

The horror of the thing bristled upon them all.

Then they heard the girl's voice upstairs calling shrilly: 'Mother, mother – who is it? Mother, who is it?'

15 Elizabeth hurried to the foot of the stairs and opened the door:

'Go to sleep!' she commanded sharply. 'What are you shouting about? Go to sleep at once – there's nothing –'

Then she began to mount the stairs. They could hear her on the boards, and on the plaster floor of the little bedroom. They could 20 hear her distinctly:

'What's the matter now? – what's the matter with you, silly thing?' – her voice was much agitated, with an unreal gentleness.

'I thought it was some men come,' said the plaintive voice of the child. 'Has he come?'

25 'Yes, they've brought him. There's nothing to make a fuss about. Go to sleep now, like a good child.'

They could hear her voice in the bedroom, they waited whilst she covered the children under the bedclothes.

'Is he drunk?' asked the girl, timidly, faintly.

30 'No! No – he's not! He – he's asleep.'

'Is he asleep downstairs?'

'Yes – and don't make a noise.'

There was silence for a moment, then the men heard the frightened child again:

35 'What's that noise?'

'It's nothing, I tell you, what are you bothering for?'

The noise was the grandmother moaning. She was oblivious of everything, sitting on her chair rocking and moaning. The manager put his hand on her arm and bade her 'Sh – sh!!'

The old woman opened her eyes and looked at him. She was shocked by this interruption, and seemed to wonder.   5

'What time is it?' – the plaintive thin voice of the child, sinking back unhappily into sleep, asked this last question.

'Ten o'clock,' answered the mother more softly. Then she must have bent down and kissed the children.

Matthews beckoned to the men to come away. They put on their   10
caps and took up the stretcher. Stepping over the body, they tiptoed out of the house. None of them spoke till they were far from the wakeful children.

When Elizabeth came down she found her mother alone on the parlour floor, leaning over the dead man, the tears dropping on   15
him.

'We must lay him out,' the wife said. She put on the kettle, then returning knelt at the feet, and began to unfasten the knotted leather laces. The room was clammy and dim with only one candle, so that she had to bend her face almost to the floor. At last she got   20
off the heavy boots and put them away.

'You must help me now,' she whispered to the old woman. Together they stripped the man.

When they arose, saw him lying in the naïve dignity of death, the women stood arrested in fear and respect. For a few moments   25
they remained still, looking down, the old mother whimpering. Elizabeth felt countermanded. She saw him, how utterly inviolable he lay in himself. She had nothing to do with him. She could not accept it. Stooping, she laid her hand on him, in claim. He was still warm, for the mine was hot where he had died. His mother had his   30
face between her hands, and was murmuring incoherently. The old tears fell in succession as drops from wet leaves; the mother was not weeping, merely her tears flowed. Elizabeth embraced the body of her husband, with cheek and lips. She seemed to be listening, inquiring, trying to get some connection. But she could   35
not. She was driven away. He was impregnable.

She rose, went into the kitchen, where she poured warm water into a bowl, brought soap and flannel and a soft towel.

'I must wash him,' she said.

Then the old mother rose stiffly, and watched Elizabeth as
5 she carefully washed his face, carefully brushing the big blond moustache from his mouth with the flannel. She was afraid with a bottomless fear, so she ministered to him. The old woman, jealous, said:

'Let me wipe him!' – and she kneeled on the other side drying
10 slowly as Elizabeth washed, her big black bonnet sometimes brushing the dark head of her daughter. They worked thus in silence for a long time. They never forgot it was death, and the touch of the man's dead body gave them strange emotions, different in each of the women; a great dread possessed them both, the
15 mother felt the lie was given to her womb, she was denied; the wife felt the utter isolation of the human soul, the child within her was a weight apart from her.

At last it was finished. He was a man of handsome body, and his face showed no traces of drink. He was blonde, full-fleshed, with
20 fine limbs. But he was dead.

'Bless him,' whispered his mother, looking always at his face, and speaking out of sheer terror. 'Dear lad – bless him!' She spoke in a faint, sibilant ecstasy of fear and mother love.

Elizabeth sank down again to the floor, and put her face against
25 his neck, and trembled and shuddered. But she had to draw away again. He was dead, and her living flesh had no place against his. A great dread and weariness held her: she was so unavailing. Her life was gone like this.

'White as milk he is, clear as a twelve-month baby, bless him,
30 the darling!' the old mother murmured to herself. 'Not a mark on him, clear and clean and white, beautiful as ever a child was made,' she murmured with pride. Elizabeth kept her face hidden.

'He went peaceful, Lizzie – peaceful as sleep. Isn't he beautiful, the lamb? Ay – he must ha' made his peace, Lizzie. 'Appen he
35 made it all right, Lizzie, shut in there. He'd have time. He wouldn't look like this if he hadn't made his peace. The lamb, the dear lamb.

Eh, but he had a hearty laugh. I loved to hear it. He had the heartiest laugh, Lizzie, as a lad – '

Elizabeth looked up. The man's mouth was fallen back, slightly open under the cover of the moustache. The eyes, half shut, did not show glazed in the obscurity. Life with its smoky burning gone 5 from him, had left him apart and utterly alien to her. And she knew what a stranger he was to her. In her womb was ice of fear, because of this separate stranger with whom she had been living as one flesh. Was this what it all meant – utter, intact separateness, obscured by heat of living? In dread she turned her face away. The fact was too 10 deadly. There had been nothing between them, and yet they had come together, exchanging their nakedness repeatedly. Each time he had taken her, they had been two isolated beings, far apart as now. He was no more responsible than she. The child was like ice in her womb. For as she looked at the dead man, her mind, cold 15 and detached, said clearly: 'Who am I? What have I been doing? I have been fighting a husband who did not exist. *He* existed all the time. What wrong have I done? What was that I have been living with? There lies the reality, this man.' – And her soul died in her for fear: she knew she had never seen him, he had never seen her, 20 they had met in the dark and had fought in the dark, not knowing whom they met nor whom they fought. And now she saw, and turned silent in seeing. For she had been wrong. She had said he was something he was not; she had felt familiar with him. Whereas he was apart all the while, living as she never lived, feeling as she 25 never felt.

In fear and shame she looked at his naked body, that she had known falsely. And he was the father of her children. Her soul was torn from her body and stood apart. She looked at his naked body and was ashamed, as if she had denied it. After all, it was itself. It 30 seemed awful to her. She looked at his face, and she turned her own face to the wall. For his look was other than hers, his way was not her way. She had denied him what he was – she saw it now. She had refused him as himself. – And this had been her life, and his life. – She was grateful to death, which restored the truth. And 35 she knew she was not dead.

And all the while her heart was bursting with grief and pity for him. What had he suffered? What stretch of horror for this helpless man! She was rigid with agony. She had not been able to help him. He had been cruelly injured, this naked man, this other being, and
5 she could make no reparation. There were the children – but the children belonged to life. This dead man had nothing to do with them. He and she were only channels through which life had flowed to issue in the children. She was a mother – but how awful she knew it now to have been a wife. And he, dead now, how awful he
10 must have felt it to be a husband. She felt that in the next world he would be a stranger to her. If they met there, in the beyond, they would only be ashamed of what had been before. The children had come, for some mysterious reason, out of both of them. But the children did not unite them. Now he was dead, she knew how
15 eternally he was apart from her, how eternally he had nothing more to do with her. She saw this episode of her life closed. They had denied each other in life. Now he had withdrawn. An anguish came over her. It was finished then: it had become hopeless between them long before he died. Yet he had been her husband. But how
20 little!

'Have you got his shirt, 'Lizabeth?'

Elizabeth turned without answering, though she strove to weep and behave as her mother-in-law expected. But she could not, she was silenced. She went into the kitchen and returned with the
25 garment.

'It is aired,' she said, grasping the cotton shirt here and there to try. She was almost ashamed to handle him; what right had she or anyone to lay hands on him; but her touch was humble on his body. It was hard work to clothe him. He was so heavy and inert.
30 A terrible dread gripped her all the while: that he could be so heavy and utterly inert, unresponsive, apart. The horror of the distance between them was almost too much for her – it was so infinite a gap she must look across.

At last it was finished. They covered him with a sheet and left
35 him lying, with his face bound. And she fastened the door of the little parlour, lest the children should see what was lying there.

Then, with peace sunk heavy on her heart, she went about making tidy the kitchen. She knew she submitted to life, which was her immediate master. But from death, her ultimate master, she winced with fear and shame.

You Touched Me

The Pottery House was a square, ugly, brick house girt in by the wall that enclosed the whole grounds of the pottery itself. To be sure, a privet hedge partly masked the house and its ground from the pottery-yard and works: but only partly. Through the hedge
5 could be seen the desolate yard, and the many-windowed, factory-like pottery, over the hedge could be seen the chimneys and the outhouses. But inside the hedge, a pleasant garden and lawn sloped down to a willow pool, which had once supplied the works.

The Pottery itself was now closed, the great doors of the yard
10 permanently shut. No more the great crates with yellow straw showing through, stood in stacks by the packing shed. No more the drays drawn by great horses rolled down the hill with a high load. No more the pottery-lasses in their clay-coloured overalls, their faces and hair splashed with grey fine mud, shrieked and
15 larked with the men. All that was over.

'We like it much better – oh, much better – quieter,' said Matilda Rockley.

'Oh, yes,' assented Emmie Rockley, her sister.

'I'm sure you do,' agreed the visitor.
20 But whether the two Rockley girls really liked it better, or whether they only imagined they did, is a question. Certainly their lives were much more grey and dreary now that the grey clay had ceased to spatter its mud and silt its dust over the premises. They did not quite realize how they missed the shrieking, shouting lasses, whom
25 they had known all their lives and disliked so much.

Matilda and Emmie were already old maids. In a thorough industrial district, it is not easy for the girls who have expectations above the common to find husbands. The ugly industrial town was full of men, young men who were ready to marry. But they were all colliers or pottery-hands, mere workmen. The Rockley girls would have about ten thousand pounds each when their father died: ten thousand pounds' worth of profitable house-property. It was not to be sneezed at: they felt so themselves, and refrained from sneezing away such a fortune on any mere member of the proletariat. Consequently, bank-clerks or nonconformist clergymen or even school-teachers having failed to come forward, Matilda had begun to give up all idea of ever leaving the Pottery House.

Matilda was a tall, thin, graceful fair girl, with a rather large nose. She was the Mary to Emmie's Martha: that is, Matilda loved painting and music, and read a good many novels, whilst Emmie looked after the house-keeping. Emmie was shorter, plumper than her sister, and she had no accomplishments. She looked up to Matilda, whose mind was naturally refined and sensible.

In their quiet, melancholy way, the two girls were happy. Their mother was dead. Their father was ill also. He was an intelligent man who had had some education, but preferred to remain as if he were one with the rest of the working people. He had a passion for music and played the violin pretty well. But now he was getting old, he was very ill, dying of a kidney disease. He had been rather a heavy whiskey-drinker.

This quiet household, with one servant-maid, lived on year after year in the Pottery House. Friends came in, the girls went out, the father drank himself more and more ill. Outside in the street there was a continual racket of the colliers and their dogs and children. But inside the pottery wall was a deserted quiet.

In all this ointment there was one little fly. Ted Rockley, the father of the girls, had had four daughters, and no son. As his girls grew, he felt angry at finding himself always in a household of women. He went off to London and adopted a boy out of a Charity Institution. Emmie was fourteen years old, and Matilda sixteen, when their father arrived home with his prodigy, the boy of six, Hadrian.

Hadrian was just an ordinary boy from a Charity Home, with ordinary brownish hair and ordinary bluish eyes and of ordinary rather cockney speech. The Rockley girls – there were three at home at the time of his arrival – had resented his being sprung on them. He, with his watchful, charity-institution instinct, knew this at once. Though he was only six years old, Hadrian had a subtle, jeering look on his face when he regarded the three young women. They insisted he should address them as Cousin: Cousin Flora, Cousin Matilda, Cousin Emmie. He complied, but there seemed a mockery in his tone.

The girls, however, were kind-hearted by nature. Flora married and left home. Hadrian did very much as he pleased with Matilda and Emmie, though they had certain strictnesses. He grew up in the Pottery House and about the Pottery premises, went to an elementary school, and was invariably called Hadrian Rockley. He regarded Cousin Matilda and Cousin Emmie with a certain laconic indifference, was quiet and reticent in his ways. The girls called him sly, but that was unjust. He was merely cautious, and without frankness. His Uncle, Ted Rockley, understood him tacitly, their natures were somewhat akin. Hadrian and the elderly man had a real but unemotional regard for one another.

When he was thirteen years old the boy was sent to a High School in the County town. He did not like it. His Cousin Matilda had longed to make a little gentleman of him, but he refused to be made. He would give a little contemptuous curve to his lip, and take on a shy, charity-boy grin, when refinement was thrust upon him. He played truant from the High School, sold his books, his cap with its badge, even his very scarf and pocket-handkerchief, to his school-fellows, and went raking off heaven knows where with the money. So he spent two very unsatisfactory years.

When he was fifteen he announced that he wanted to leave England to go to the Colonies. He had kept touch with the Home. The Rockleys knew that, when Hadrian made a declaration, in his quiet, half-jeering manner, it was worse than useless to oppose him. So at last the boy departed, going to Canada under the protection of the Institution to which he had belonged. He said good-bye to the Rockleys without a word of thanks, and parted, it seemed without a pang. Matilda and Emmie wept often to think of how he left them: even on their father's face a queer look came. But Hadrian wrote fairly regularly from Canada. He had entered some electricity works near Montreal, and was doing well. 5

At last, however, the war came. In his turn, Hadrian joined up and came to Europe. The Rockleys saw nothing of him. They lived on, just the same, in the Pottery House. Ted Rockley was dying of a sort of dropsy, and in his heart he wanted to see the boy. When the armistice was signed, Hadrian had a long leave, and wrote that 10 he was coming home to the Pottery House.

The girls were terribly fluttered. To tell the truth, they were a little afraid of Hadrian. Matilda, tall and thin, was frail in her health, both girls were worn with nursing their father. To have Hadrian, a young man of twenty-one, in the house with them, 15 after he had left them so coldly five years before, was a trying circumstance.

They were in a flutter. Emmie persuaded her father to have his bed made finally in the morning-room downstairs, whilst his room upstairs was prepared for Hadrian. This was done, and prep- 20 arations were going on for the arrival, when, at ten o'clock in the morning the young man suddenly turned up, quite unexpectedly. Cousin Emmie, with her hair bobbed up in absurd little bobs round her forehead, was busily polishing the stair-rods, while Cousin Matilda was in the kitchen washing the drawing-room ornaments 25 in a lather, her sleeves rolled back on her thin arms, and her head tied up oddly and coquettishly in a duster.

Cousin Matilda blushed deep with mortification when the self-possessed young man walked in with his kit-bag, and put his cap on the sewing machine. He was little and self-confident, with a 30 curious neatness about him that still suggested the Charity Institution. His face was brown, he had a small moustache, he was vigorous enough in his smallness.

'*Well*, is it Hadrian!' exclaimed Cousin Matilda, wringing the lather off her hand. 'We didn't expect you till to-morrow.' 35

'I got off Monday night,' said Hadrian, glancing round the room.

'Fancy!' said Cousin Matilda. Then, having dried her hands, she went forward, held out her hand, and said:

'How are you?'

'Quite well, thank you,' said Hadrian.

5 'You're quite a man,' said Cousin Matilda.

Hadrian glanced at her. She did not look her best: so thin, so large-nosed, with that pink-and-white checked duster tied round her head. She felt her disadvantage. But she had had a good deal of suffering and sorrow, she did not mind any more.

10 The servant entered – one that did not know Hadrian.

'Come and see my father,' said Cousin Matilda.

In the hall they roused Cousin Emmie like a partridge from cover. She was on the stairs pushing the bright stair-rods into place. Instinctively her hand went to the little knobs, her front hair bobbed

15 on her forehead.

'Why!' she exclaimed crossly. 'What have you come to-day for?'

'I got off a day earlier,' said Hadrian, and his man's voice so deep and unexpected was like a blow to Cousin Emmie.

'Well, you've caught us in the midst of it,' she said, with resent-

20 ment. Then all three went into the middle room.

Mr Rockley was dressed – that is, he had on his trousers and socks – but he was resting on the bed, propped up just under the window, from whence he could see his beloved and resplendent garden, where tulips and apple-trees were ablaze. He did not look

25 as ill as he was, for the water puffed him up, and his face kept its colour. His stomach was much swollen. He glanced round swiftly, turning his eyes without turning his head. He was the wreck of a handsome, well-built man.

Seeing Hadrian, a queer, unwilling smile went over his face. The

30 young man greeted him sheepishly.

'You wouldn't make a life-guardsman,' he said. 'Do you want something to eat?'

Hadrian looked round – as if for the meal.

'I don't mind,' he said.

35 'What shall you have – egg and bacon?' asked Emmie shortly.

'Yes, I don't mind,' said Hadrian.

The sisters went down to the kitchen, and sent the servant to finish the stairs.

'Isn't he *altered*?' said Matilda, *sotto voce.*

'Isn't he!' said Cousin Emmie. '*What* a little man!'

They both made a grimace, and laughed nervously.   5

'Get the frying-pan,' said Emmie to Matilda.

'But he's as cocky as ever,' said Matilda, narrowing her eyes and shaking her head knowingly, as she handed the frying-pan.

'Mannie!' said Emmie sarcastically. Hadrian's new-fledged, cocksure manliness evidently found no favour in her eyes.   10

'Oh, he's not bad,' said Matilda. 'You don't want to be prejudiced against him.'

'I'm not prejudiced against him, I think he's all right for looks,' said Emmie, 'but there's too much of the little mannie about him.'   15

'Fancy catching us like this,' said Matilda.

'They've no thought for anything,' said Emmie with contempt. 'You go up and get dressed, our Matilda. I don't care about him. I can see to things, and you can talk to him. I shan't.'

'He'll talk to my father,' said Matilda, meaningful.   20

'*Sly – !*' exclaimed Emmie, with a grimace.

The sisters believed that Hadrian had come hoping to get something out of their father – hoping for a legacy. And they were not at all sure he would not get it.

Matilda went upstairs to change. She had thought it all out how 25
she would receive Hadrian, and impress him. And he had caught her with her head tied up in a duster, and her thin arms in a basin of lather. But she did not care. She now dressed herself most scrupulously, carefully folded her long, beautiful, blonde hair, touched her pallor with a little rouge, and put her long string of 30
exquisite crystal beads over her soft green dress. Now she looked elegant, like a heroine in a magazine illustration, and almost as unreal.

She found Hadrian and her father talking away. The young man was short of speech as a rule, but he could find his tongue with his 35
'uncle'. They were both sipping a glass of brandy, and smoking,

and chatting like a pair of old cronies. Hadrian was telling about Canada. He was going back there when his leave was up.

'You wouldn't like to stop in England, then?' said Mr Rockley.

'No, I wouldn't stop in England,' said Hadrian.

5 'How's that? There's plenty of electricians here,' said Mr Rockley.

'Yes. But there's too much difference between the men and the employers over here – too much of that for me,' said Hadrian.

The sick man looked at him narrowly, with oddly smiling 10 eyes.

'That's it, is it?' he replied.

Matilda heard and understood. 'So that's your big idea, is it, my little man,' she said to herself. She had always said of Hadrian that he had no proper *respect* for anybody or anything, that he was sly 15 and *common*. She went down to the kitchen for a *sotto voce* confab with Emmie.

'He thinks a rare lot of himself!' she whispered.

'He's somebody, he is!' said Emmie with contempt.

'He thinks there's too much difference between masters and 20 men, over here,' said Matilda.

'Is it any different in Canada?' asked Emmie.

'Oh, yes – democratic,' replied Matilda. 'He thinks they're all on a level over there.'

'Ay, well he's over here now,' said Emmie drily, 'so he can keep 25 his place.'

As they talked they saw the young man sauntering down the garden, looking casually at the flowers. He had his hands in his pockets, and his soldier's cap neatly on his head. He looked quite at his ease, as if in possession. The two women, flustered, watched 30 him through the window.

'We know what he's come for,' said Emmie, churlishly. Matilda looked a long time at the neat khaki figure. It had something of the charity boy about it still; but now it was a man's figure, laconic, charged with plebeian energy. She thought of the derisive passion 35 in his voice as he had declaimed against the propertied classes, to her father.

'You don't know, Emmie. Perhaps he's not come for that,' she rebuked her sister. They were both thinking of the money.

They were still watching the young soldier. He stood away at the bottom of the garden, with his back to them, his hands in his pockets, looking into the water of the willow pond. Matilda's dark-blue eyes had a strange, full look in them, the lids, with the faint blue veins showing, dropped rather low. She carried her head light and high, but she had a look of pain. The young man at the bottom of the garden turned and looked up the path. Perhaps he saw them through the window. Matilda moved into shadow.

That afternoon their father seemed weak and ill. He was easily exhausted. The doctor came, and told Matilda that the sick man might die suddenly at any moment – but then he might not. They must be prepared.

So the day passed, and the next. Hadrian made himself at home. He went about in the morning in his brownish jersey and his khaki trousers, collarless, his bare neck showing. He explored the pottery premises, as if he had some secret purpose in so doing, he talked with Mr Rockley, when the sick man had strength. The two girls were always angry when the two men sat talking together like cronies. Yet it was chiefly a kind of politics they talked.

On the second day after Hadrian's arrival, Matilda sat with her father in the evening. She was drawing a picture which she wanted to copy. It was very still, Hadrian was gone out somewhere, no one knew where, and Emmie was busy. Mr Rockley reclined on his bed, looking out in silence over his evening-sunny garden.

'If anything happens to me, Matilda,' he said, 'you won't sell this house – you'll stop here –'

Matilda's eyes took their slightly haggard look as she stared at her father.

'Well, we couldn't do anything else,' she said.

'You don't know what you might do,' he said. 'Everything is left to you and Emmie, equally. You do as you like with it – only don't sell this house, don't part with it.'

'No,' she said.

'And give Hadrian my watch and chain, and a hundred pounds

out of what's in the bank – and help him if he ever wants helping. I haven't put his name in the will.'

'Your watch and chain, and a hundred pounds – yes. But you'll be here when he goes back to Canada, father.'

5 'You never know what'll happen,' said her father.

Matilda sat and watched him, with her full, haggard eyes, for a long time, as if tranced. She saw that he knew he must go soon – she saw like a clairvoyant.

Later on she told Emmie what her father had said about the 10 watch and chain and the money.

'What right has *he*' – *he* – meaning Hadrian – 'to my father's watch and chain – what has it to do with him? Let him have the money, and get off,' said Emmie. She loved her father.

That night Matilda sat late in her room. Her heart was anxious 15 and breaking, her mind seemed entranced. She was too much entranced even to weep, and all the time she thought of her father, only her father. At last she felt she must go to him.

It was near midnight. She went along the passage and to his room. There was a faint light from the moon outside. She listened 20 at his door. Then she softly opened and entered. The room was faintly dark. She heard a movement on the bed.

'Are you asleep?' she said softly, advancing to the side of the bed.

'Are you asleep?' she repeated gently, as she stood at the side of 25 the bed. And she reached her hand in the darkness to touch his fore-head. Delicately, her fingers met the nose and the eyebrows, she laid her fine, delicate hand on his brow. It seemed fresh and smooth – very fresh and smooth. A sort of surprise stirred her, in her entranced state. But it could not waken her. Gently, she leaned over the bed 30 and stirred her fingers over the low-growing hair on his brow.

'Can't you sleep to-night?' she said.

There was a quick stirring in the bed. 'Yes, I can,' a voice answered. It was Hadrian's voice. She started away. Instantly, she was awakened from her late-at-night trance. She remembered that 35 her father was downstairs, that Hadrian had his room. She stood in the darkness as if stung.

'Is it you, Hadrian?' she said. 'I thought it was my father.' She was so startled, so shocked, that she could not move. The young man gave an uncomfortable laugh, and turned in his bed.

At last she got out of the room. When she was back in her own room, in the light, and her door was closed, she stood holding up her hand that had touched him, as if it were hurt. She was almost too shocked, she could not endure.

'Well,' said her calm and weary mind, 'it was only a mistake, why take any notice of it.'

But she could not reason her feelings so easily. She suffered, feeling herself in a false position. Her right hand, which she had laid so gently on his face, on his fresh skin, ached now, as if it were really injured. She could not forgive Hadrian for the mistake: it made her dislike him deeply.

Hadrian too slept badly. He had been awakened by the opening of the door, and had not realized what the question meant. But the soft, straying tenderness of her hand on his face startled something out of his soul. He was a charity boy, aloof and more or less at bay. The fragile exquisiteness of her caress startled him most, revealed unknown things to him.

In the morning she could feel the consciousness in his eyes, when she came downstairs. She tried to bear herself as if nothing at all had happened, and she succeeded. She had the calm self-control, self-indifference, of one who has suffered and borne her suffering. She looked at him from her darkish, almost drugged blue eyes, she met the spark of consciousness in his eyes, and quenched it. And with her long, fine hand she put the sugar in his coffee.

But she could not control him as she thought she could. He had a keen memory stinging his mind, a new set of sensations working in his consciousness. Something new was alert in him. At the back of his reticent, guarded mind he kept his secret alive and vivid. She was at his mercy, for he was unscrupulous, his standard was not her standard.

He looked at her curiously. She was not beautiful, her nose was too large, her chin was too small, her neck was too thin. But her skin was clear and fine, she had a high-bred sensitiveness. This

5

10

15

20

25

30

35

41

queer, brave, high-bred quality she shared with her father. The charity boy could see it in her tapering fingers, which were white and ringed. The same glamour that he knew in the elderly man he now saw in the woman. And he wanted to possess himself of it, he wanted to make himself master of it. As he went about through the old pottery-yard, his secretive mind schemed and worked. To be master of that strange soft delicacy such as he had felt in her hand upon his face, – this was what he set himself towards. He was secretly plotting.

He watched Matilda as she went about, and she became aware of his attention, as of some shadow following her. But her pride made her ignore it. When he sauntered near her, his hands in his pockets, she received him with that same commonplace kindliness which mastered him more than any contempt. Her superior breeding seemed to control him. She made herself feel towards him exactly as she had always felt: he was a young boy who lived in the house with them, but was a stranger. Only, she dared not remember his face under her hand. When she remembered that, she was bewildered. Her hand had offended her, she wanted to cut it off. And she wanted, fiercely, to cut off the memory in him. She assumed she had done so.

One day, when he sat talking with his 'uncle', he looked straight into the eyes of the sick man, and said:

'But I shouldn't like to live and die here in Rawsley.'

'No – well – you needn't,' said the sick man.

'Do you think Cousin Matilda likes it?'

'I should think so.'

'I don't call it much of a life,' said the youth. 'How much older is she than me, Uncle?'

The sick man looked at the young soldier.

'A good bit,' he said.

'Over thirty?' said Hadrian.

'Well, not so much. She's thirty-two.'

Hadrian considered a while.

'She doesn't look it,' he said.

Again the sick father looked at him.

'Do you think she'd like to leave here?' said Hadrian.

'Nay, I don't know,' replied the father, restive.

Hadrian sat still, having his own thoughts. Then in a small, quiet voice, as if he were speaking from inside himself, he said:

'I'd marry her if you wanted me to.'

The sick man raised his eyes suddenly, and stared. He stared for a long time. The youth looked inscrutably out of the window.

'*You!*' said the sick man, mocking, with some contempt. Hadrian turned and met his eyes. The two men had an inexplicable understanding.

'If you wasn't against it,' said Hadrian.

'Nay,' said the father, turning aside, 'I don't think I'm against it. I've never thought of it. But – But Emmie's the youngest.'

He had flushed, and looked suddenly more alive. Secretly he loved the boy.

'You might ask her,' said Hadrian.

The elder man considered.

'Hadn't you better ask her yourself?' he said.

'She'd take more notice of you,' said Hadrian.

They were both silent. Then Emmie came in.

For two days Mr Rockley was excited and thoughtful. Hadrian went about quietly, secretly, unquestioning. At last the father and daughter were alone together. It was very early morning, the father had been in much pain. As the pain abated, he lay still, thinking.

'Matilda!' he said suddenly, looking at his daughter.

'Yes, I'm here,' she said.

'Ay! I want you to do something –'

She rose in anticipation.

'Nay, sit still. I want you to marry Hadrian –'

She thought he was raving. She rose, bewildered and frightened.

'Nay, sit you still, sit you still. You hear what I tell you.'

'But you don't know what you're saying, father.'

'Ay, I know well enough. I want you to marry Hadrian, I tell you.'

She was dumbfounded. He was a man of few words.

'You'll do what I tell you,' he said.

She looked at him slowly.

'What put such an idea in your mind?' she said proudly.

'He did.'

Matilda almost looked her father down, her pride was so
5 offended.

'Why, it's disgraceful,' she said.

'Why?'

She watched him slowly.

'What do you ask me for?' she said. 'It's disgusting.'

10 'The lad's sound enough,' he replied, testily.

'You'd better tell him to clear out,' she said, coldly.

He turned and looked out of the window. She sat flushed and
erect for a long time. At length her father turned to her, looking
really malevolent.

15 'If you won't,' he said, 'you're a fool, and I'll make you pay for
your foolishness, do you see?'

Suddenly a cold fear gripped her. She could not believe her
senses. She was terrified and bewildered. She stared at her father,
believing him to be delirious, or mad, or drunk. What could she
20 do?

'I tell you,' he said. 'I'll send for Whittle tomorrow if you don't.
You shall neither of you have anything of mine.'

Whittle was the solicitor. She understood her father well enough:
he would send for his solicitor, and make a will leaving all his
25 property to Hadrian: neither she nor Emmie should have anything.
It was too much. She rose and went out of the room, up to her own
room, where she locked herself in.

She did not come out for some hours. At last, late at night, she
confided in Emmie.

30 'The sliving demon, he wants the money,' said Emmie. 'My
father's out of his mind.'

The thought that Hadrian merely wanted the money was another
blow to Matilda. She did not love the impossible youth – but she
had not yet learned to think of him as a thing of evil. He now
35 became hideous to her mind.

Emmie had a little scene with her father next day.

'You don't mean what you said to our Matilda yesterday, do you, father?' she asked aggressively.

'Yes,' he replied.

'What, that you'll alter your will?'

'Yes.'

'You won't,' said his angry daughter.

But he looked at her with a malevolent little smile.

'Annie!' he shouted. 'Annie!'

He had still power to make his voice carry. The servant maid came in from the kitchen.

'Put your things on, and go down to Whittle's office, and say I want to see Mr Whittle as soon as he can, and will he bring a will-form.'

The sick man lay back a little – he could not lie down. His daughter sat as if she had been struck. Then she left the room.

Hadrian was pottering about in the garden. She went straight down to him.

'Here,' she said. 'You'd better get off. You'd better take your things and go from here, quick.'

Hadrian looked slowly at the infuriated girl.

'Who says so?' he asked.

'*We* say so – get off, you've done enough mischief and damage.'

'Does Uncle say so?'

'Yes, he does.'

'I'll go and ask him.'

But like a fury Emmie barred his way.

'No, you needn't. You needn't ask him nothing at all. We don't want you, so you can go.'

'Uncle's boss here.'

'A man that's dying, and you crawling round and working on him for his money! – you're not fit to live.'

'Oh!' he said. 'Who says I'm working for his money?'

'I say. But my father told our Matilda, and *she* knows what you are. *She* knows what you're after. So you might as well clear out, for all you'll get – guttersnipe!'

He turned his back on her, to think. It had not occurred to him that they would think he was after the money. He *did* want the money – badly. He badly wanted to be an employer himself, not one of the employed. But he knew, in his subtle, calculating way, that it was not for money he wanted Matilda. He wanted both the money and Matilda. But he told himself the two desires were 5 separate, not one. He could not do with Matilda, *without* the money. But he did not want her *for* the money.

When he got this clear in his mind, he sought for an opportunity to tell it her, lurking and watching. But she avoided him. In the evening the lawyer came. Mr Rockley seemed to have a new access 10 of strength – a will was drawn up, making the previous arrangements wholly conditional. The old will held good, if Matilda would consent to marry Hadrian. If she refused then at the end of six months the whole property passed to Hadrian.

Mr Rockley told this to the young man, with malevolent satisfac- 15 tion. He seemed to have a strange desire, quite unreasonable, for revenge upon the women who had surrounded him for so long, and served him so carefully.

'Tell her in front of me,' said Hadrian.

So Mr Rockley sent for his daughters.

20 At last they came, pale, mute, stubborn. Matilda seemed to have retired far off, Emmie seemed like a fighter ready to fight to the death. The sick man reclined on the bed, his eyes bright, his puffed hand trembling. But his face had again some of its old, bright handsomeness. Hadrian sat quiet, a little aside: the indomitable, 25 dangerous charity boy.

'There's the will,' said their father, pointing them to the paper.

The two women sat mute and immovable, they took no notice.

'Either you marry Hadrian, or he has everything,' said the father with satisfaction.

30 'Then let him have everything,' said Matilda coldly.

'He's not! He's not!' cried Emmie fiercely. 'He's not going to have it. The guttersnipe!'

An amused look came on her father's face.

'You hear that, Hadrian,' he said.

35 'I didn't offer to marry Cousin Matilda for the money,' said Hadrian, flushing and moving on his seat.

Matilda looked at him slowly, with her dark-blue, drugged eyes.
He seemed a strange little monster to her.

'Why, you liar, you know you did,' cried Emmie.

The sick man laughed. Matilda continued to gaze strangely at
the young man.   5

'She knows I didn't,' said Hadrian.

He too had his courage, as a rat has indomitable courage in the
end. Hadrian had some of the neatness, the reserve, the underground quality of the rat. But he had perhaps the ultimate courage,
the most unquenchable courage of all.   10

Emmie looked at her sister.

'Oh, well,' she said. 'Matilda – don't you bother. Let him have
everything, we can look after ourselves.'

'I know he'll take everything,' said Matilda, abstractedly.

Hadrian did not answer. He knew in fact that if Matilda refused   15
him he would take everything, and go off with it.

'A clever little mannie –!' said Emmie, with a jeering grimace.

The father laughed noiselessly to himself. But he was tired . . .

'Go on, then,' he said. 'Go on, let me be quiet.'

Emmie turned and looked at him.   20

'You deserve what you've got,' she said to her father bluntly.

'Go on,' he answered mildly. 'Go on.'

Another night passed – a night nurse sat up with Mr Rockley.
Another day came. Hadrian was there as ever, in his woollen jersey
and coarse khaki trousers and bare neck. Matilda went about, frail   25
and distant, Emmie black-browed in spite of her blondeness. They
were all quiet, for they did not intend the mystified servant to learn
anything.

Mr Rockley had very bad attacks of pain, he could not breathe.
The end seemed near. They all went about quiet and stoical, all   30
unyielding. Hadrian pondered within himself. If he did not marry
Matilda he would go to Canada with twenty thousand pounds.
This was itself a very satisfactory prospect. If Matilda consented
he would have nothing – she would have her own money.

Emmie was the one to act. She went off in search of the solicitor   35
and brought him home with her. There was an interview, and

47

Whittle tried to frighten the youth into withdrawal – but without avail. The clergyman and relatives were summoned – but Hadrian stared at them and took no notice. It made him angry, however.

He wanted to catch Matilda alone. Many days went by, and he was not successful: she avoided him. At last, lurking, he surprised her one day as she came to pick gooseberries, and he cut off her retreat. He came to the point at once.

'You don't want me, then?' he said, in his subtle, insinuating voice.

'I don't want to speak to you,' she said, averting her face.

'You put your hand on me, though,' he said. 'You shouldn't have done that, and then I should never have thought of it. You shouldn't have touched me.'

'If you were anything decent, you'd know that was a mistake, and forget it,' she said.

'I know it was a mistake – but I shan't forget it. If you wake a man up, he can't go to sleep again because he's told to.'

'If you had any decent feeling in you, you'd have gone away,' she replied.

'I didn't want to,' he replied.

She looked away into the distance. At last she asked:

'What do you persecute me for, if it isn't for the money. I'm old enough to be your mother. In a way I've been your mother.'

'Doesn't matter,' he said. 'You've been no mother to me. Let us marry and go out to Canada – you might as well – you've touched me.'

She was white and trembling. Suddenly she flushed with anger.

'It's so *indecent*,' she said.

'How?' he retorted. 'You touched me.'

But she walked away from him. She felt as if he had trapped her. He was angry and depressed, he felt again despised.

That same evening she went into her father's room.

'Yes,' she said suddenly. 'I'll marry him.'

Her father looked up at her. He was in pain, and very ill.

'You like him now, do you?' he said, with a faint smile.

She looked down into his face, and saw death not far off. She turned and went coldly out of the room.

The solicitor was sent for, preparations were hastily made. In all the interval Matilda did not speak to Hadrian, never answered him if he addressed her. He approached her in the morning. 5

'You've come round to it, then?' he said, giving her a pleasant look from his twinkling, almost kindly eyes. She looked down at him and turned aside. She looked down on him both literally and figuratively. Still he persisted, and triumphed.

Emmie raved and wept, the secret flew abroad. But Matilda was 10 silent and unmoved. Hadrian was quiet and satisfied, and nipped with fear also. But he held out against his fear. Mr Rockley was very ill, but unchanged.

On the third day the marriage took place. Matilda and Hadrian drove straight home from the registrar, and went straight into the 15 room of the dying man. His face lit up with a clear twinkling smile.

'Hadrian, – you've got her?' he said, a little hoarsely.

'Yes,' said Hadrian, who was pale round the gills.

'Ay, my lad, I'm glad you're mine,' replied the dying man. Then he turned his eyes closely on Matilda. 20

'Let's look at you, Matilda,' he said. Then his voice went strange and unrecognizable. 'Kiss me,' he said.

She stooped and kissed him. She had never kissed him before, not since she was a tiny child. But she was quiet, very still.

'Kiss him,' the dying man said. 25

Obediently, Matilda put forward her mouth and kissed the young husband.

'That's right! That's right!' murmured the dying man.

The Fox

The two girls were usually known by their surnames, Banford and
March. They had taken the farm together, intending to work it all
by themselves: that is, they were going to rear chickens, make a
living by poultry, and add to this by keeping a cow, and raising one
5 or two young beasts. Unfortunately things did not turn out well.

Banford was a small, thin, delicate thing with spectacles. She,
however, was the principal investor, for March had little or no
money. Banford's father, who was a tradesman in Islington, gave
his daughter the start, for her health's sake, and because he loved
10 her, and because it did not look as if she would marry. March was
more robust. She had learned carpentry and joinery at the evening
classes in Islington. She would be the man about the place. They
had, moreover, Banford's old grandfather living with them at the
start. He had been a farmer. But unfortunately the old man died
15 after he had been at Bailey Farm for a year. Then the two girls
were left alone.

They were neither of them young: that is, they were near thirty.
But they certainly were not old. They set out quite gallantly with
their enterprise. They had numbers of chickens, black Leghorns
20 and white Leghorns, Plymouths and Wyandottes; also some ducks;
also two heifers in the fields. One heifer, unfortunately, refused
absolutely to stay in the Bailey Farm closes. No matter how March
made up the fences, the heifer was out, wild in the woods, or
trespassing on the neighbouring pasture, and March and Banford
25 were away, flying after her, with more haste than success. So this
heifer they sold in despair. Then, just before the other beast was
expecting her first calf, the old man died, and the girls, afraid of

the coming event, sold her in a panic, and limited their attentions to fowls and ducks.

In spite of a little chagrin, it was a relief to have no more cattle on hand. Life was not made merely to be slaved away. Both girls agreed in this. The fowls were quite enough trouble. March had set up her carpenter's bench at the end of the open shed. Here she worked, making coops and doors and other appurtenances. The fowls were housed in the bigger building, which had served as barn and cowshed in old days. They had a beautiful home, and should have been perfectly content. Indeed, they looked well enough. But the girls were disgusted at their tendency to strange illnesses, at their exacting way of life, and at their refusal, obstinate refusal to lay eggs.

March did most of the outdoor work. When she was out and about, in her puttees and breeches, her belted coat and her loose cap, she looked almost like some graceful, loose-balanced young man, for her shoulders were straight, and her movements easy and confident, even tinged with a little indifference, or irony. But her face was not a man's face, ever. The wisps of her crisp dark hair blew about her as she stooped, her eyes were big and wide and dark, when she looked up again, strange, startled, shy and sardonic at once. Her mouth, too, was almost pinched as if in pain and irony. There was something odd and unexplained about her. She would stand balanced on one hip, looking at the fowls pattering about in the obnoxious fine mud of the sloping yard, and calling to her favourite white hen, which came in answer to her name. But there was an almost satirical flicker in March's big, dark eyes as she looked at her three-toed flock pottering about under her gaze, and the same slight dangerous satire in her voice as she spoke to the favoured Patty, who pecked at March's boot by way of friendly demonstration.

Fowls did not flourish at Bailey Farm, in spite of all that March did for them. When she provided hot food for them, in the morning, according to rule, she noticed that it made them heavy and dozy for hours. She expected to see them lean against the pillars of the shed in their languid processes of digestion. And she knew quite well that they ought to be busily scratching and foraging about, if they were to come to any good. So she decided to give them their hot food at night, and let them sleep on it. Which she did. But it made no difference.

5 War conditions, again, were very unfavourable to poultry keeping. Food was scarce and bad. And when the Daylight Saving Bill was passed, the fowls obstinately refused to go to bed as usual, about nine o'clock in the summer-time. That was late enough, indeed, for there was no peace till they were shut up and asleep.
10 Now they cheerfully walked around, without so much as glancing at the barn, until ten o'clock or later. Both Banford and March disbelieved in living for work alone. They wanted to read or take a cycle-ride in the evening, or perhaps March wished to paint curvilinear swans on porcelain, with green background, or else
15 make a marvellous fire-screen by processes of elaborate cabinet work. For she was a creature of odd whims and unsatisfied tendencies. But from all these things she was prevented by the stupid fowls.

One evil there was greater than any other. Bailey Farm was
20 a little homestead, with ancient wooden barn and two-gabled farm-house, lying just one field removed from the edge of the wood. Since the War the fox was a demon. He carried off the hens under the very noses of March and Banford. Banford would start and stare through her big spectacles with all her eyes, as another
25 squawk and flutter took place at her heels. Too late! Another white Leghorn gone. It was disheartening.

They did what they could to remedy it. When it became permitted to shoot foxes, they stood sentinel with their guns, the two of them, at the favoured hours. But it was no good. The fox was
30 too quick for them. So another year passed, and another, and they were living on their losses, as Banford said. They let their farm-house one summer, and retired to live in a railway-carriage that was deposited as a sort of out-house in a corner of the field. This amused them, and helped their finances. None the less, things
35 looked dark.

Although they were usually the best of friends, because Banford, though nervous and delicate, was a warm, generous soul, and March, though so odd and absent in herself, had a strange magnanimity, yet, in the long solitude, they were apt to become a little irritable with one another, tired of one another. March had four-fifths of the work to do, and though she did not mind, there seemed no relief, and it made her eyes flash curiously sometimes. Then Banford, feeling more nerve-worn than ever, would become despondent, and March would speak sharply to her. They seemed to be losing ground, somehow, losing hope as the months went by. There alone in the fields by the wood, with the wide country stretching hollow and dim to the round hills of the White Horse, in the far distance, they seemed to have to live too much off themselves. There was nothing to keep them up – and no hope.

The fox really exasperated them both. As soon as they had let the fowls out, in the early summer mornings, they had to take their guns and keep guard: and then again, as soon as evening began to mellow, they must go once more. And he was so sly. He slid along in the deep grass, he was difficult as a serpent to see. And he seemed to circumvent the girls deliberately. Once or twice March had caught sight of the white tip of his brush, or the ruddy shadow of him in the deep grass, and she had let fire at him. But he made no account of this.

One evening March was standing with her back to the sunset, her gun under her arm, her hair pushed under her cap. She was half watching, half musing. It was her constant state. Her eyes were keen and observant, but her inner mind took no notice of what she saw. She was always lapsing into this odd, rapt state, her mouth rather screwed up. It was a question, whether she was there, actually consciously present, or not.

The trees on the wood-edge were a darkish, brownish green in the full light – for it was the end of August. Beyond, the naked, copper-like shafts and limbs of the pine-trees shone in the air. Nearer the rough grass, with its long brownish stalks all agleam, was full of light. The fowls were round about – the ducks were still swimming on the pond under the pine-trees. March looked at it all, saw it all, and did not see it. She heard Banford speaking to the fowls, in the distance – and she did not hear. What was she thinking about? Heaven knows. Her consciousness was, as it were, held back.

She lowered her eyes, and suddenly saw the fox. He was looking up at her. His chin was pressed down, and his eyes were looking up. They met her eyes. And he knew her. She was spell-bound – she knew he knew her. So he looked into her eyes, and her soul failed her. He knew her, he was not daunted.

She struggled, confusedly she came to herself, and saw him making off, with slow leaps over some fallen boughs, slow, impudent jumps. Then he glanced over his shoulder, and ran smoothly away. She saw his brush held smooth like a feather, she saw his white buttocks twinkle. And he was gone, softly, soft as the wind.

She put her gun to her shoulder, but even then pursed her mouth, knowing it was nonsense to pretend to fire. So she began to walk slowly after him, in the direction he had gone, slowly, pertinaciously. She expected to find him. In her heart she was determined to find him. What she would do when she saw him again she did not consider. But she was determined to find him. So she walked abstractedly about on the edge of the wood, with wide, vivid dark eyes, and a faint flush in her cheeks. She did not think. In strange mindlessness she walked hither and thither.

At last she became aware that Banford was calling her. She made an effort of attention, turned, and gave some sort of screaming call in answer. Then again she was striding off towards the homestead. The red sun was setting, the fowls were retiring towards their roost. She watched them, white creatures, black creatures, gathering to the barn. She watched them spell-bound, without seeing them. But her automatic intelligence told her when it was time to shut the door.

She went indoors to supper, which Banford had set on the table. Banford chatted easily. March seemed to listen, in her distant, manly way. She answered a brief word now and then. But all the time she was as if spell-bound. And as soon as supper was over, she rose again to go out, without saying why.

She took her gun again and went to look for the fox. For he had lifted his eyes upon her, and his knowing look seemed to have entered her brain. She did not so much think of him: she was possessed by him. She saw his dark, shrewd, unabashed eye looking into her, knowing her. She felt him invisibly master her spirit. She knew the way he lowered his chin as he looked up, she knew his muzzle, the golden brown, and the greyish white. And again she saw him glance over his shoulder at her, half inviting, half contemptuous and cunning. So she went, with her great startled eyes glowing, her gun under her arm, along the wood edge. Meanwhile the night fell, and a great moon rose above the pine trees. And again Banford was calling.

So she went indoors. She was silent and busy. She examined her gun, and cleaned it, musing abstractedly by the lamplight. Then she went out again, under the great moon, to see if everything was right. When she saw the dark crests of the pine-trees against the blood-red sky, again her heart beat to the fox, the fox. She wanted to follow him, with her gun.

It was some days before she mentioned the affair to Banford. Then suddenly, one evening she said:

'The fox was right at my feet on Saturday night.'

'Where?' said Banford, her eyes opening behind her spectacles.

'When I stood just above the pond.'

'Did you fire?' cried Banford.

'No, I didn't.'

'Why not?'

'Why, I was too much surprised, I suppose.'

It was the same old, slow, laconic way of speech March always had. Banford stared at her friend for a few moments.

'You saw him?' she cried.

'Oh yes! He was looking up at me, cool as anything.'

'I tell you,' cried Banford – 'the cheek! – They're not afraid of us, Nellie.'

'Oh, no,' said March.

'Pity you didn't get a shot at him,' said Banford.

'Isn't it a pity! I've been looking for him ever since. But I don't suppose he'll come so near again.'

'I don't suppose he will,' said Banford.

And she proceeded to forget about it, except that she was more indignant than ever at the impudence of the beggars. March was also not conscious that she thought of the fox. But whenever she fell into her half-musing, when she was half rapt, and half intelligently aware of what passed under her vision, then it was the fox which somehow dominated her unconsciousness, possessed the blank half of her musing. And so it was for weeks, and months. No matter whether she had been climbing the trees for the apples, or beating down the last of the damsons, or whether she had been digging out the ditch from the duck-pond, or clearing out the barn, when she had finished, or when she straightened herself, and pushed the wisps of hair away again from her forehead, and pursed up her mouth again in an odd, screwed fashion, much too old for her years, there was sure to come over her mind the old spell of the fox, as it came when he was looking at her. It was as if she could smell him at these times. And it always recurred, at unexpected moments, just as she was going to sleep at night, or just as she was pouring the water into the tea-pot, to make tea – it was the fox, it came over her like a spell.

So the months passed. She still looked for him unconsciously when she went towards the wood. He had become a settled effect in her spirit, a state permanently established, not continuous, but always recurring. She did not know what she felt or thought: only the state came over her, as when he looked at her.

The months passed, the dark evenings came, heavy, dark November, when March went about in high boots, ankle deep in mud, when the night began to fall at four o'clock, and the day never properly dawned. Both girls dreaded these times. They dreaded the almost continuous darkness that enveloped them on their desolate little farm near the wood. Banford was physically afraid. She was afraid of tramps, afraid lest someone should come prowling around. March was not so much afraid, as uncomfortable, and disturbed. She felt discomfort and gloom in all her physique.

Usually the two girls had tea in the sitting-room. March lighted a fire at dusk, and put on the wood she had chopped and sawed during the day. Then the long evening was in front, dark, sodden, black outside, lonely and rather oppressive inside, a little dismal. March was content not to talk, but Banford could not keep still. Merely listening to the wind in the pines outside, or the drip of water, was too much for her.

One evening the girls had washed up the tea-things in the kitchen, and March had put on her house-shoes, and taken up a roll of crochet-work, which she worked at slowly from time to time. So she lapsed into silence. Banford stared at the red fire, which, being of wood, needed constant attention. She was afraid to begin to read too early, because her eyes would not bear any strain. So she sat staring at the fire, listening to the distant sounds, sound of cattle lowing, of a dull, heavy moist wind, of the rattle of the evening train on the little railway not far off. She was almost fascinated by the red glow of the fire.

Suddenly both girls started, and lifted their heads. They heard a footstep – distinctly a footstep. Banford recoiled in fear. March stood listening. Then rapidly she approached the door that led into the kitchen. At the same time they heard the footsteps approach the back door. They waited a second. The back door opened softly. Banford gave a loud cry. A man's voice said softly:

'Hello!'

March recoiled, and took a gun from a corner.

'What do you want?' she cried, in a sharp voice.

Again the soft, softly-vibrating man's voice said:

'Hello! What's wrong?'

'I shall shoot!' cried March. 'What do you want?'

'Why, what's wrong? What's wrong?' come the soft, wondering, rather scared voice: and a young soldier, with his heavy kit on his back, advanced into the dim light.

'Why,' he said, 'who lives here then?'

'We live here,' said March. 'What do you want?'

'Oh!' came the long, melodious, wonder-note from the young soldier. 'Doesn't William Grenfel live here then?'

'No – you know he doesn't.'

'Do I? – Do I? I don't, you see. – He *did* live here, because he

5

10

15

20

25

30

35

57

was my grandfather, and I lived here myself five years ago. What's become of him then?'

The young man – or youth, for he would not be more than twenty, now advanced and stood in the inner doorway. March, already under the influence of his strange, soft, modulated voice, stared at him spell-bound. He had a ruddy, roundish face, with fairish hair, rather long, flattened to his forehead with sweat. His eyes were blue, and very bright and sharp. On his cheeks, on the fresh ruddy skin were fine, fair hairs, like a down, but sharper. It gave him a slightly glistening look. Having his heavy sack on his shoulders, he stooped, thrusting his head forward. His hat was loose in one hand. He stared brightly, very keenly from girl to girl, particularly at March, who stood pale, with great dilated eyes, in her belted coat and puttees, her hair knotted in a big crisp knot behind. She still had the gun in her hand. Behind her, Banford, clinging to the sofa-arm, was shrinking away, with half-averted head.

'I thought my grandfather still lived here? – I wonder if he's dead.'

'We've been here for three years,' said Banford, who was beginning to recover her wits, seeing something boyish in the round head with its rather long sweaty hair.

'Three years! You don't say so! – And you don't know who was here before you?'

'I know it was an old man, who lived by himself.'

'Ay! Yes, that's him! – And what became of him then?'

'He died. – I know he died –'

'Ay! He's dead then!'

The youth stared at them without changing colour or expression. If he had any expression, besides a slight baffled look of wonder, it was one of sharp curiosity concerning the two girls; sharp, impersonal curiosity, the curiosity of that round young head.

But to March he was the fox. Whether it was the thrusting forward of his head, or the glisten of fine whitish hairs on the ruddy cheek-bones, or the bright, keen eyes, that can never be said: but the boy was to her the fox, and she could not see him otherwise.

'How is it you didn't know if your grandfather was alive or dead?' asked Banford, recovering her natural sharpness.

'Ay, that's it,' replied the softly-breathing youth. 'You see, I joined up in Canada, and I hadn't heard for three or four years. – I ran away to Canada.'

'And now have you just come from France?'

'Well – from Salonika really.'

There was a pause, nobody knowing quite what to say.

'So you've nowhere to go now?' said Banford rather lamely.

'Oh, I know some people in the village. Anyhow, I can go to the "Swan".'

'You came on the train, I suppose. – Would you like to sit down a bit?'

'Well – I don't mind.'

He gave an odd little groan as he swung off his kit. Banford looked at March.

'Put the gun down,' she said. 'We'll make a cup of tea.'

'Ay,' said the youth. 'We've seen enough of rifles.'

He sat down rather tired on the sofa, leaning forward.

March recovered her presence of mind, and went into the kitchen. There she heard the soft young voice musing:

'Well, to think I should come back and find it like this!' He did not seem sad, not at all – only rather interestedly surprised.

'And what a difference in the place, eh?' he continued, looking round the room.

'You see a difference, do you?' said Banford.

'Yes, – don't I!'

His eyes were unnaturally clear and bright, though it was the brightness of abundant health.

March was busy in the kitchen preparing another meal. It was about seven o'clock. All the time, while she was active, she was attending to the youth in the sitting-room, not so much listening to what he said, as feeling the soft run of his voice. She primmed up her mouth tighter and tighter, puckering it as if it were sewed, in her effort to keep her will uppermost. Yet her large eyes dilated and glowed in spite of her, she lost herself. Rapidly and carelessly

she prepared the meal, cutting large chunks of bread and margarine
– for there was no butter. She racked her brain to think of something
else to put on the tray – she had only bread, margarine, and jam,
and the larder was bare. Unable to conjure anything up, she went
5 into the sitting-room with her tray.

She did not want to be noticed. Above all, she did not want him
to look at her. But when she came in, and was busy setting the
table just behind him, he pulled himself up from his sprawling, and
turned and looked over his shoulder. She became pale and wan.

10 The youth watched her as she bent over the table, looked at her
slim, well-shapen legs, at the belted coat dropping around her
thighs, at the knot of dark hair, and his curiosity, vivid and widely
alert, was again arrested by her.

The lamp was shaded with a dark-green shade, so that the light
15 was thrown downwards, the upper half of the room was dim. His
face moved bright under the light, but March loomed shadowy in
the distance.

She turned round, but kept her eyes sideways, dropping and
lifting her dark lashes. Her mouth unpuckered, as she said to
20 Banford:

'Will you pour out?'

Then she went into the kitchen again.

'Have your tea where you are, will you?' said Banford to the
youth – 'unless you'd rather come to the table.'

25 'Well,' said he, 'I'm nice and comfortable here, aren't I? I will
have it here, if you don't mind.'

'There's nothing but bread and jam,' she said. And she put his
plate on a stool by him. She was very happy now, waiting on him.
For she loved company. And now she was no more afraid of him
30 than if he were her own younger brother. He was such a boy.

'Nellie,' she called. 'I've poured you a cup out.'

March appeared in the doorway, took her cup, and sat down in
a corner, as far from the light as possible. She was very sensitive in
her knees. Having no skirts to cover them, and being forced to sit
35 with them boldly exposed, she suffered. She shrank and shrank,
trying not to be seen. And the youth, sprawling low on the couch,

glanced up at her, with long, steady, penetrating looks, till she was almost ready to disappear. Yet she held her cup balanced, she drank her tea, screwed up her mouth and held her head averted. Her desire to be invisible was so strong that it quite baffled the youth. He felt he could not see her distinctly. She seemed like a shadow within the shadow. And ever his eyes came back to her, searching, unremitting, with unconscious fixed attention.

Meanwhile he was talking softly and smoothly to Banford, who loved nothing so much as gossip, and who was full of perky interest, like a bird. Also he ate largely and quickly and voraciously, so that March had to cut more chunks of bread and margarine, for the roughness of which Banford apologized.

'Oh, well,' said March, suddenly speaking, 'if there's no butter to put on it, it's no good trying to make dainty pieces.'

Again the youth watched her, and he laughed, with a sudden, quick laugh, showing his teeth and wrinkling his nose.

'It isn't, is it,' he answered in his soft, near voice.

It appeared he was Cornish by birth and upbringing. When he was twelve years old he had come to Bailey Farm with his grandfather, with whom he had never agreed very well. So he had run away to Canada, and worked far away in the West. Now he was here – and that was the end of it.

He was very curious about the girls, to find out exactly what they were doing. His questions were those of a farm youth; acute, practical, a little mocking. He was very much amused by their attitude to their losses: for they were amusing on the score of heifers and fowls.

'Oh, well,' broke in March, 'we don't believe in living for nothing but work.'

'Don't you?' he answered. And again the quick young laugh came over his face. He kept his eyes steadily on the obscure woman in the corner.

'But what will you do when you've used up all your capital?' he said.

'Oh, I don't know,' answered March laconically. 'Hire ourselves out for landworkers, I suppose.'

'Yes, but there won't be any demand for women landworkers now the war's over,' said the youth.

'Oh, we'll see. We shall hold on a bit longer yet,' said March, with a plangent, half-sad, half-ironical indifference.

5 'There wants a man about the place,' said the youth softly. Banford burst out laughing.

'Take care what you say,' she interrupted. 'We consider ourselves quite efficient.'

'Oh,' came March's slow, plangent voice, 'it isn't a case of
10 efficiency, I'm afraid. If you're going to do farming you must be at it from morning till night, and you might as well be a beast yourself.'

'Yes, that's it,' said the youth. 'You aren't willing to put your-selves into it.'

'We aren't,' said March, 'and we know it.'

15 'We want some of our time for ourselves,' said Banford.

The youth threw himself back on the sofa, his face tight with laughter, and laughed silently but thoroughly. The calm scorn of the girls tickled him tremendously.

'Yes,' he said, 'but why did you begin then?'

20 'Oh,' said March, 'we had a better opinion of the nature of fowls then, than we have now.'

'Of Nature altogether, I'm afraid,' said Banford. 'Don't talk to me about Nature.'

Again the face of the youth tightened with delighted laughter.

25 'You haven't a very high opinion of fowls and cattle, have you?' he said.

'Oh no – quite a low one,' said March.

He laughed out.

'Neither fowls nor heifers,' said Banford, 'nor goats nor the
30 weather.'

The youth broke into a sharp yap of laughter, delighted. The girls began to laugh too, March turning aside her face and wrinkling her mouth in amusement.

'Oh, well,' said Banford, 'we don't mind, do we, Nellie?'

35 'No,' said March, 'we don't mind.'

The youth was very pleased. He had eaten and drunk his fill.

Banford began to question him. His name was Henry Grenfel –
no, he was not called Harry, always Henry. He continued to answer
with courteous simplicity, grave and charming. March, who was
not included, cast long, slow glances at him from her recess, as he
sat there on the sofa, his hands clasping his knees, his face under 5
the lamp bright and alert, turned to Banford. She became almost
peaceful, at last. He was identified with the fox – and he was here
in full presence. She need not go after him any more. There in the
shadow of her corner she gave herself up to a warm, relaxed peace,
almost like sleep, accepting the spell that was on her. But she 10
wished to remain hidden. She was only fully at peace whilst he
forgot her, talking to Banford. Hidden in the shadow of the corner,
she need not any more be divided in herself, trying to keep up two
planes of consciousness. She could at last lapse into the odour of
the fox. 15

For the youth, sitting before the fire in his uniform, sent a faint
but distinct odour into the room, indefinable, but something like
a wild creature. March no longer tried to reserve herself from it.
She was still and soft in her corner like a passive creature in its
cave. 20

At last the talk dwindled. The youth relaxed his clasp of his
knees, pulled himself together a little, and looked round. Again he
became aware of the silent, half-invisible woman in the corner.

'Well,' he said, unwillingly, 'I suppose I'd better be going, or
they'll be in bed at the "Swan".' 25

'I'm afraid they're in bed anyhow,' said Banford. 'They've all
got this influenza.'

'Have they!' he exclaimed. And he pondered. 'Well,' he continued, 'I shall find a place somewhere.'

'I'd say you could stay here, only –' Banford began. 30

He turned and watched her, holding his head forward.

'What –?' he asked.

'Oh, well,' she said, 'propriety, I suppose –' She was rather
confused.

'It wouldn't be improper, would it?' he said, gently surprised. 35

'Not as far as we're concerned,' said Banford.

'And not as far as *I'm* concerned,' he said, with grave naïveté. 'After all, it's my own home, in a way.'

Banford smiled at this.

'It's what the village will have to say,' she said.

5 There was a moment's blank pause.

'What do you say, Nellie?' asked Banford.

'I don't mind,' said March, in her distinct tone. 'The village doesn't matter to me, anyhow.'

'No,' said the youth, quick and soft. 'Why should it? – I mean,
10 what should they say?'

'Oh, well,' came March's plangent, laconic voice, 'they'll easily find something to say. But it makes no difference, what they say. We can look after ourselves.'

'Of course you can,' said the youth.

15 'Well then, stop if you like,' said Banford. 'The spare room is quite ready.'

His face shone with pleasure.

'If you're quite sure it isn't troubling you too much,' he said, with that soft courtesy which distinguished him.

20 'Oh, it's no trouble,' they both said.

He looked, smiling with delight, from one to another.

'It's awfully nice not to have to turn out again, isn't it?' he said gratefully.

'I suppose it is,' said Banford.

25 March disappeared to attend the room. Banford was as pleased and thoughtful as if she had her own brother home from France. It gave her just the same kind of gratification to attend on him, to get out the bath for him, and everything. Her natural warmth and kindliness had now an outlet. And the youth luxuriated in her
30 sisterly attention. But it puzzled him slightly to know that March was silently working for him too. She was so curiously silent and obliterated. It seemed to him he had not really seen her. He felt he should not know her if he met her in the road.

That night March dreamed vividly. She dreamed she heard a
35 singing outside, which she could not understand, a singing that roamed round the house, in the fields and in the darkness. It moved

her so, that she felt she must weep. She went out, and suddenly she knew it was the fox singing. He was very yellow and bright, like corn. She went nearer to him, but he ran away and ceased singing. He seemed near, and she wanted to touch him. She stretched out her hand, but suddenly he bit her wrist, and at the same instant, as she drew back, the fox, turning round to bound away, whisked his brush across her face, and it seemed his brush was on fire, for it seared and burned her mouth with a great pain. She awoke with the pain of it, and lay trembling as if she were really seared.

In the morning, however, she only remembered it as a distant memory. She arose and was busy preparing the house and attending to the fowls. Banford flew into the village on her bicycle, to try and buy food. She was a hospitable soul. But alas, in the year 1918 there was not much food to buy. The youth came downstairs in his shirt-sleeves. He was young and fresh, but he walked with his head thrust forward, so that his shoulders seemed raised and rounded, as if he had a slight curvature of the spine. It must have been only a manner of bearing himself, for he was young and vigorous. He washed himself and went outside, whilst the women were preparing breakfast.

He saw everything, and examined everything. His curiosity was quick and insatiable. He compared the state of things with that which he remembered before, and cast over in his mind the effect of the changes. He watched the fowls and the ducks, to see their condition, he noticed the flight of wood-pigeons overhead: they were very numerous; he saw the few apples high up, which March had not been able to reach; he remarked that they had borrowed a draw-pump, presumably to empty the big soft-water cistern which was on the north side of the house.

'It's a funny, dilapidated old place,' he said to the girls, as he sat at breakfast.

His eyes were wise and childish, with thinking about things. He did not say much, but ate largely. March kept her face averted. She, too, in the early morning, could not be aware of him, though something about the glint of his khaki reminded her of the brilliance of her dream-fox.

During the day the girls went about their business. In the morning, he attended to the guns, shot a rabbit and a wild duck that was flying high, towards the wood. That was a great addition to the empty larder. The girls felt that already he had earned his keep.
5 He said nothing about leaving, however. In the afternoon he went to the village. He came back at tea-time. He had the same alert, forward-reaching look on his roundish face. He hung his hat on a peg with a little swinging gesture. He was thinking about something.

10 'Well,' he said to the girls, as he sat at table. 'What am I going to do?'

'How do you mean – what are you going to do?' said Banford.

'Where am I going to find a place in the village, to stay?' he said.

'I don't know,' said Banford. 'Where do you think of staying?'

15 'Well –' he hesitated – 'at the "Swan" they've got this flu, and at the "Plough and Harrow" they've got the soldiers who are collecting the hay for the army: besides in the private houses, there's ten men and a corporal altogether billeted in the village, they tell me. I'm not sure where I could get a bed.'

20 He left the matter to them. He was rather calm about it. March sat with her elbows on the table, her two hands supporting her chin, looking at him unconsciously. Suddenly he lifted his clouded blue eyes, and unthinking looked straight into March's eyes. He was startled as well as she. He, too, recoiled a little. March felt the
25 same sly, taunting, knowing spark leap out of his eyes as he turned his head aside, and fall into her soul, as it had fallen from the dark eyes of the fox. She pursed her mouth as if in pain, as if asleep too.

'Well, I don't know –' Banford was saying. She seemed reluct-
30 ant, as if she were afraid of being imposed upon. She looked at March. But, with her weak, troubled sight, she only saw the usual semi-abstraction on her friend's face. 'Why don't you speak, Nellie?' she said.

But March was wide-eyed and silent, and the youth, as if fasci-
35 nated, was watching her without moving his eyes.

'Go on – answer something,' said Banford. And March turned

her head slightly aside, as if coming to consciousness, or trying to come to consciousness.

'What do you expect me to say?' she asked automatically.

'Say what you think,' said Banford.

'It's all the same to me,' said March. 5

And again there was silence. A pointed light seemed to be on the boy's eyes, penetrating like a needle.

'So it is to me,' said Banford. 'You can stop on here if you like.'

A smile like a cunning little flame came over his face, suddenly and involuntarily. He dropped his head quickly to hide it, and 10 remained with his head dropped, his face hidden.

'You can stop on here if you like. You can please yourself, Henry,' Banford concluded.

Still he did not reply, but remained with his head dropped. Then he lifted his face. It was bright with a curious light, as if exultant, 15 and his eyes were strangely clear as he watched March. She turned her face aside, her mouth suffering as if wounded, and her consciousness dim.

Banford became a little puzzled. She watched the steady, pellucid gaze of the youth's eyes, as he looked at March, with the invisible 20 smile gleaming on his face. She did not know how he was smiling, for no feature moved. It seemed only in the gleam, almost the glitter of the fine hairs on his cheeks. Then he looked with quite a changed look, at Banford.

'I'm sure,' he said in his soft, courteous voice, 'you're awfully 25 good. You're too good. You don't want to be bothered with me, I'm sure.'

'Cut a bit of bread, Nellie,' said Banford uneasily; adding: 'It's no bother, if you like to stay. It's like having my own brother here for a few days. He's a boy like you are.' 30

'That's awfully kind of you,' the lad repeated. 'I should like to stay, ever so much, if you're sure I'm not a trouble to you.'

'No, of course you're no trouble. I tell you, it's a pleasure to have somebody in the house beside ourselves,' said warm-hearted Banford. 35

'But Miss March?' he said in his soft voice, looking at her.

'Oh, it's quite all right as far as I'm concerned,' said March vaguely.

His face beamed, and he almost rubbed his hands with pleasure.

'Well then,' he said, 'I should love it, if you'd let me pay my
5 board and help with the work.'

'You've no need to talk about board,' said Banford.

One or two days went by, and the youth stayed on at the farm. Banford was quite charmed by him. He was so soft and courteous in speech, not wanting to say much himself, preferring to hear what
10 she had to say, and to laugh in his quick, half-mocking way. He helped readily with the work – but not too much. He loved to be out alone with the gun in his hands, to watch, to see. For his sharp-eyed, impersonal curiosity was insatiable, and he was most free when he was quite alone, half-hidden, watching.

15 Particularly he watched March. She was a strange character to him. Her figure, like a graceful young man's, piqued him. Her dark eyes made something rise in his soul, with a curious elate excitement, when he looked into them, an excitement he was afraid to let be seen, it was so keen and secret. And then her odd, shrewd
20 speech made him laugh outright. He felt he must go further, he was inevitably impelled. But he put away the thought of her, and went off towards the wood's edge with the gun.

The dusk was falling as he came home, and with the dusk, a fine, late November rain. He saw the fire-light leaping in the window of
25 the sitting-room, a leaping light in the little cluster of the dark buildings. And he thought to himself, it would be a good thing to have this place for his own. And then the thought entered him shrewdly: why not marry March? He stood still in the middle of the field for some moments, the dead rabbit hanging still in his
30 hand, arrested by this thought. His mind waited in amazement – it seemed to calculate – and then he smiled curiously to himself in acquiescence. Why not? Why not, indeed? It was a good idea. What if it was rather ridiculous? What did it matter? What if she was older than he? It didn't matter. When he thought of her dark,
35 startled, vulnerable eyes he smiled subtly to himself. He was older than she, really. He was master of her.

He scarcely admitted his intention even to himself. He kept it as a secret even from himself. It was all too uncertain as yet. He would have to see how things went. Yes, he would have to see how things went. If he wasn't careful, she would just simply mock at the idea. He knew, sly and subtle as he was, that if he went to her plainly and said: 'Miss March, I love you and want you to marry me,' her inevitable answer would be: 'Get out. I don't want any of that tomfoolery.' This was her attitude to men and their 'tomfoolery'. If he was not careful, she would turn round on him with her savage, sardonic ridicule, and dismiss him from the farm and from her own mind, for ever. He would have to go gently. He would have to catch her as you catch a deer or a woodcock when you go out shooting. It's no good walking out into the forest and saying to the deer: 'Please fall to my gun.' No, it is a slow, subtle battle. When you really go out to get a deer, you gather yourself together, you coil yourself inside yourself, and you advance secretly, before dawn, into the mountains. It is not so much what you do, when you go out hunting, as how you feel. You have to be subtle and cunning and absolutely fatally ready. It becomes like a fate. Your own fate overtakes and determines the fate of the deer you are hunting. First of all, even before you come in sight of your quarry, there is a strange battle, like mesmerism. Your own soul, as a hunter, has gone out to fasten on the soul of the deer, even before you see any deer. And the soul of the deer fights to escape. Even before the deer has any wind of you, it is so. It is a subtle, profound battle of wills, which takes place in the invisible. And it is a battle never finished till your bullet goes home. When you are *really* worked up to the true pitch, and you come at last into range, you don't then aim as you do when you are firing at a bottle. It is your own *will* which carries the bullet into the heart of your quarry. The bullet's flight home is a sheer projection of your own fate into the fate of the deer. It happens like a supreme wish, a supreme act of volition, not as a dodge of cleverness.

He was a huntsman in spirit, not a farmer, and not a soldier stuck in a regiment. And it was as a young hunter, that he wanted to bring down March as his quarry, to make her his wife. So he gathered himself subtly together, seemed to withdraw into a kind of invisibility. He was not quite sure how he would go on. And March was suspicious as a hare. So he remained in appearance just the nice, odd stranger-youth, staying for a fortnight on the place.

5   He had been sawing logs for the fire, in the afternoon. Darkness came very early. It was still a cold, raw mist. It was getting almost too dark to see. A pile of short sawed logs lay beside the trestle. March came to carry them indoors, or into the shed, as he was busy sawing the last log. He was working in his shirt-sleeves, and
10 did not notice her approach. She came unwillingly, as if shy. He saw her stooping to the bright-ended logs, and he stopped sawing. A fire like lightning flew down his legs in the nerves.

'March?' he said, in his quiet young voice.

She looked up from the logs she was piling.

15   'Yes!' she said.

He looked down on her in the dusk. He could see her not too distinctly.

'I wanted to ask you something,' he said.

'Did you? What was it?' she said. Already the fright was in her
20 voice. But she was too much mistress of herself.

'Why –' his voice seemed to draw out soft and subtle, it penetrated her nerves – 'why, what do you think it is?'

She stood up, placed her hands on her hips, and stood looking at him transfixed, without answering. Again he burned with a
25 sudden power.

'Well,' he said and his voice was so soft it seemed rather like a subtle touch, like the merest touch of a cat's paw, a feeling rather than a sound. 'Well – I wanted to ask you to marry me.'

March felt rather than heard him. She was trying in vain to turn
30 aside her face. A great relaxation seemed to have come over her. She stood silent, her head slightly on one side. He seemed to be bending towards her, invisibly smiling. It seemed to her fine sparks came out of him.

Then very suddenly, she said:

35   'Don't try any of your tomfoolery on me.'

A quiver went over his nerves. He had missed. He waited a

moment to collect himself again. Then he said, putting all the strange softness into his voice, as if he were imperceptibly stroking her:

'Why, it's not tomfoolery. It's not tomfoolery. I mean it. I mean it. What makes you disbelieve me?' 5

He sounded hurt. And his voice had such a curious power over her; making her feel loose and relaxed. She struggled somewhere for her own power. She felt for a moment that she was lost – lost – lost. The word seemed to rock in her as if she were dying. Suddenly again she spoke. 10

'You don't know what you are talking about,' she said, in a brief and transient stroke of scorn. 'What nonsense! I'm old enough to be your mother.'

'Yes, I do know what I'm talking about. Yes, I do,' he persisted softly, as if he were producing his voice in her blood. 'I know quite 15 well what I'm talking about. You're not old enough to be my mother. That isn't true. And what does it matter even if it was. You can marry me whatever age we are. What is age to me? And what is age to you! Age is nothing.'

A swoon went over her as he concluded. He spoke rapidly – in 20 the rapid Cornish fashion – and his voice seemed to sound in her somewhere where she was helpless against it. 'Age is nothing!' The soft, heavy insistence of it made her sway dimly out there in the darkness. She could not answer.

A great exultance leaped like fire over his limbs. He felt he had 25 won.

'I want to marry you, you see. Why shouldn't I?' he proceeded, soft and rapid. He waited for her to answer. In the dusk he saw her almost phosphorescent. Her eyelids were dropped, her face half-averted and unconscious. She seemed to be in his power. But 30 he waited, watchful. He dared not yet touch her.

'Say then,' he said. 'Say then you'll marry me. Say – say?' He was softly insistent.

'What?' she asked, faint, from a distance, like one in pain. His voice was now unthinkably near and soft. He drew very near 35 to her.

'Say yes.'

'Oh, I can't,' she wailed helplessly, half articulate, as if semi-conscious, and as if in pain, like one who dies. 'How can I?'

'You can,' he said softly, laying his hand gently on her shoulder as she stood with her head averted and dropped, dazed. 'You can. Yes, you can. What makes you say you can't? You can. You can.' And with awful softness he bent forward and just touched her neck with his mouth and his chin.

'Don't!' she cried, with a faint mad cry like hysteria, starting away and facing round on him. 'What do you mean?' But she had no breath to speak with. It was as if she was killed.

'I mean what I say,' he persisted softly and cruelly. 'I want you to marry me. I want you to marry me. You know that, now, don't you? You know that, now? Don't you? Don't you?'

'What?' she said.

'Know,' he replied.

'Yes,' she said. 'I know you say so.'

'And you know I mean it, don't you?'

'I know you say so.'

'You believe me?' he said.

She was silent for some time. Then she pursed her lips.

'I don't know what I believe,' she said.

'Are you out there?' came Banford's voice, calling from the house.

'Yes, we're bringing in the logs,' he answered.

'I thought you'd gone lost,' said Banford disconsolately. 'Hurry up, do, and come and let's have tea. The kettle's boiling.'

He stooped at once, to take an armful of little logs and carry them into the kitchen, where they were piled in a corner. March also helped, filling her arms and carrying the logs on her breast as if they were some heavy child. The night had fallen cold.

When the logs were all in, the two cleaned their boots noisily on the scraper outside, then rubbed them on the mat. March shut the door and took off her old felt hat – her farm-girl hat. Her thick, crisp black hair was loose, her face was pale and strained. She pushed back her hair vaguely, and washed her hands. Banford came hurrying into the dimly-lighted kitchen, to take from the oven the scones she was keeping hot.

'Whatever have you been doing all this time?' she asked fretfully. 'I thought you were never coming in. And it's ages since you stopped sawing. What were you doing out there?'

'Well,' said Henry, 'we had to stop that hole in the barn, to keep the rats out.'

'Why, I could see you standing there in the shed. I could see your shirt-sleeves,' challenged Banford.

'Yes, I was just putting the saw away.'

They went in to tea. March was quite mute. Her face was pale and strained and vague. The youth, who always had the same ruddy, self-contained look on his face, as though he were keeping himself to himself, had come to tea in his shirt-sleeves as if he were at home. He bent over his plate as he ate his food.

'Aren't you cold?' said Banford spitefully. 'In your shirt-sleeves.'

He looked up at her, with his chin near his plate, and his eyes very clear, pellucid, and unwavering as he watched her.

'No, I'm not cold,' he said with his usual soft courtesy. 'It's much warmer in here than it is outside, you see.'

'I hope it is,' said Banford, feeling nettled by him. He had a strange, suave assurance, and a wide-eyed bright look that got on her nerves this evening.

'But perhaps,' he said softly and courteously, 'you don't like me coming to tea without my coat. I forgot that.'

'Oh, I don't mind,' said Banford: although she *did*.

'I'll go and get it, shall I?' he said.

March's eyes turned slowly down to him.

'No, don't you bother,' she said in her queer, twanging tone. 'If you feel all right as you are, stop as you are.' She spoke with a crude authority.

'Yes,' said he, 'I *feel* all right, if I'm not rude.'

'It's usually considered rude,' said Banford. 'But we don't mind.'

'Go along, "considered rude",' ejaculated March. 'Who considers it rude?'

'Why you do, Nellie, in anybody else,' said Banford, bridling a little behind her spectacles, and feeling her food stick in her throat.

But March had again gone vague and unheeding, chewing her food as if she did not know she was eating at all. And the youth looked from one to another, with bright, watchful eyes.

Banford was offended. For all his suave courtesy and soft voice, the youth seemed to her impudent. She did not like to look at him. She did not like to meet his clear, watchful eyes, she did not like to see the strange glow in his face, his cheeks with their delicate fine hair, and his ruddy skin that was quite dull and yet which seemed to burn with a curious heat of life. It made her feel a little ill to look at him: the quality of his physical presence was too penetrating, too hot.

After tea the evening was very quiet. The youth rarely went into the village. As a rule he read: he was a great reader, in his own hours. That is, when he did begin, he read absorbedly. But he was not very eager to begin. Often he walked about the fields and along the hedges alone in the dark at night, prowling with a queer instinct for the night, and listening to the wild sounds.

Tonight, however, he took a Captain Mayne Reid book from Banford's shelf and sat down with knees wide apart and immersed himself in his story. His brownish fair hair was long, and lay on his head like a thick cap, combed sideways. He was still in his shirt-sleeves, and bending forward under the lamplight, with his knees stuck wide apart and the book in his hand and his whole figure absorbed in the rather strenuous business of reading, he gave Banford's sitting-room the look of a lumber-camp. She resented this. For on her sitting-room floor she had a red Turkey rug and dark stain round, the fire-place had fashionable green tiles, the piano stood open with the latest dance-music: she played quite well: and on the walls were March's hand-painted swans and water-lilies. Moreover, with the logs nicely, tremulously burning in the grate, the thick curtains drawn, the doors all shut, and the pine-trees hissing and shuddering in the wind outside, it was cosy, it was refined and nice. She resented the big, raw, long-legged youth sticking his khaki knees out and sitting there with his soldier's shirt-cuffs buttoned on his thick red wrists. From time to time he turned a page, and from time to time he gave a sharp look at the fire, settling the logs. Then he immersed himself again in the intense and isolated business of reading.

March, on the far side of the table, was spasmodically crocheting. 5
Her mouth was pursed in an odd way, as when she had dreamed the fox's brush burned it, her beautiful, crisp black hair strayed in wisps. But her whole figure was absorbed in its bearing, as if she herself was miles away. In a sort of semi-dream she seemed to be hearing the fox singing round the house in the wind, singing wildly 10
and sweetly and like a madness. With red but well-shaped hands she slowly crocheted the white cotton, very slowly, awkwardly.

Banford was also trying to read, sitting in her low chair. But between those two she felt fidgety. She kept moving and looking round and listening to the wind, and glancing secretly from one to 15
the other of her companions. March, seated on a straight chair, with her knees in their close breeches crossed, and slowly, laboriously crocheting, was also a trial.

'Oh dear!' said Banford. 'My eyes are bad tonight.' And she pressed her fingers on her eyes. 20

The youth looked up at her with his clear bright look, but did not speak.

'Are they, Jill?' said March absently.

Then the youth began to read again, and Banford perforce returned to her book. But she could not keep still. After a while 25
she looked up at March, and a queer, almost malignant little smile was on her thin face.

'A penny for them, Nell,' she said suddenly.

March looked round with big, startled black eyes, and went pale as if with terror. She had been listening to the fox singing so 30
tenderly, so tenderly, as he wandered round the house.

'What?' she said vaguely.

'A penny for them,' said Banford sarcastically. 'Or two-pence, if they're as deep as all that.'

The youth was watching with bright clear eyes from beneath 35
the lamp.

'Why,' came March's vague voice, 'what do you want to waste your money for?'

'I thought it would be well spent,' said Banford.

'I wasn't thinking of anything except the way the wind was
5 blowing,' said March.

'Oh dear,' replied Banford, 'I could have had as original thoughts as that myself. I'm afraid I *have* wasted my money this time.'

'Well, you needn't pay,' said March.

The youth suddenly laughed. Both women looked at him: March
10 rather surprised-looking, as if she had hardly known he was there.

'Why, do you ever pay up on these occasions?' he asked.

'Oh yes,' said Banford. 'We always do. I've sometimes had to pass a shilling a week to Nellie, in the wintertime. It costs much less in summer.'

15 'What, paying for each other's thoughts?' he laughed.

'Yes, when we've absolutely come to the end of everything else.'

He laughed quickly, wrinkling his nose sharply like a puppy and laughing with quick pleasure, his eyes shining.

'It's the first time I ever heard of that,' he said.

20 'I guess you'd hear of it often enough if you stayed a winter on Bailey Farm,' said Banford lamentably.

'Do you get so tired, then?' he asked.

'So bored,' said Banford.

'Oh!' he said gravely. 'But why should you be bored?'

25 'Who wouldn't be bored?' said Banford.

'I'm sorry to hear that,' he said gravely.

'You must be, if you were hoping to have a lively time here,' said Banford.

He looked at her long and gravely.

30 'Well,' he said, with his odd young seriousness, 'it's quite lively enough for me.'

'I'm glad to hear it,' said Banford.

And she returned to her book. In her thin, frail hair were already many threads of grey, though she was not yet thirty. The boy did not
35 look down, but turned his eyes to March, who was sitting with pursed mouth laboriously crocheting, her eyes wide and absent. She had a

warm, pale, fine skin, and a delicate nose. Her pursed mouth looked shrewish. But the shrewish look was contradicted by the curious lifted arch of her dark brows, and the wideness of her eyes; a look of startled wonder and vagueness. She was listening again for the fox, who seemed to have wandered farther off into the night.

From under the edge of the lamp-light the boy sat with his face looking up, watching her silently, his eyes round and very clear and intent. Banford, biting her fingers irritably, was glancing at him under her hair. He sat there perfectly still, his ruddy face tilted up from the low level under the light, on the edge of the dimness, and watching with perfect abstract intentness. March suddenly lifted her great dark eyes from her crotcheting, and saw him. She started, giving a little exclamation.

'There he *is*!' she cried involuntarily, as if terribly startled.

Banford looked round in amazement, sitting up straight.

'Whatever has got you, Nellie?' she cried.

But March, her face flushed a delicate rose colour, was looking away to the door.

'Nothing! Nothing!' she said crossly. 'Can't one speak?'

'Yes, if you speak sensibly,' said Banford. 'What ever did you mean?'

'I don't know what I meant,' cried March testily.

'Oh, Nellie, I hope you aren't going jumpy and nervy. I feel I can't stand another *thing*! – Whoever did you mean? Did you mean Henry?' cried poor frightened Banford.

'Yes. I suppose so,' said March laconically. She would never confess to the fox.

'Oh dear, my nerves are all gone for tonight,' wailed Banford.

At nine o'clock March brought in a tray with bread and cheese and tea – Henry had confessed that he liked a cup of tea. Banford drank a glass of milk, and ate a little bread. And soon she said:

'I'm going to bed, Nellie. I'm all nerves tonight. Are you coming?'

'Yes, I'm coming the minute I've taken the tray away,' said March.

'Don't be long then,' said Banford fretfully. 'Good-night, Henry. You'll see the fire is safe, if you come up last, won't you?'

'Yes, Miss Banford, I'll see it's safe,' he replied in his reassuring way.

March was lighting the candle to go to the kitchen. Banford took her candle and went upstairs. When March came back to the fire
5 she said to him:

'I suppose we can trust you to put out the fire and everything?' She stood there with her hand on her hip, and one knee loose, her head averted shyly, as if she could not look at him. He had his face lifted, watching her.

10 'Come and sit down a minute,' he said softly.

'No, I'll be going. Jill will be waiting, and she'll get upset if I don't come.'

'What made you jump like that this evening?' he asked.

'When did I jump?' she retorted, looking at him.

15 'Why, just now you did,' he said. 'When you cried out.'

'Oh!' she said. 'Then! – Why, I thought you were the fox!' And her face screwed into a queer smile, half ironic.

'The fox! Why the fox?' he asked softly.

'Why, one evening last summer when I was out with the gun I saw
20 the fox in the grass nearly at my feet, looking straight up at me. I don't know – I suppose he made an impression on me.' She turned aside her head again, and let one foot stray loose, self-consciously.

'And did you shoot him?' asked the boy.

'No, he gave me such a start, staring straight at me as he did,
25 and then stopping to look back at me over his shoulder with a laugh on his face.'

'A laugh on his face!' repeated Henry, also laughing. 'He frightened you, did he?'

'No, he didn't frighten me. He made an impression on me, that's
30 all.'

'And you thought I was the fox, did you?' he laughed, with the same queer, quick little laugh, like a puppy wrinkling its nose.

'Yes, I did, for the moment,' she said. 'Perhaps he'd been in my mind without my knowing.'

35 'Perhaps you think I've come to steal your chickens or something,' he said, with the same young laugh.

But she only looked at him with a wide, dark, vacant eye.

'It's the first time,' he said, 'that I've ever been taken for a fox. Won't you sit down for a minute?' His voice was very soft and cajoling.

'No,' she said. 'Jill will be waiting.' But still she did not go, but stood with one foot loose and her face turned aside, just outside the circle of light.

'But won't you answer my question?' he said, lowering his voice still more.

'I don't know what question you mean.'

'Yes, you do. Of course you do. I mean the question of you marrying me.'

'No, I shan't answer that question,' she said flatly.

'Won't you?' The queer young laugh came on his nose again. 'Is it because I'm like the fox? Is that why?' And still he laughed.

She turned and looked at him with a long, slow look.

'I wouldn't let that put you against me,' he said. 'Let me turn the lamp low, and come and sit down a minute.'

He put his red hand under the glow of the lamp, and suddenly made the light very dim. March stood there in the dimness quite shadowy, but unmoving. He rose silently to his feet, on his long legs. And now his voice was extraordinarily soft and suggestive, hardly audible.

'You'll stay a moment,' he said. 'Just a moment.' And he put his hand on her shoulder. – She turned her face from him. 'I'm sure you don't really think I'm like the fox,' he said, with the same softness and with a suggestion of laughter in his tone, a subtle mockery. 'Do you now?' – and he drew her gently towards him and kissed her neck, softly. She winced and trembled and hung away. But his strong young arm held her, and he kissed her softly again, still on the neck, for her face was averted.

'Won't you answer my question? Won't you now?' came his soft, lingering voice. He was trying to draw her near to kiss her face. And he kissed her cheek softly, near the ear.

At that moment Banford's voice was heard calling fretfully, crossly from upstairs.

'There's Jill!' cried March, starting and drawing erect.

And as she did so, quick as lightning he kissed her on the mouth, with a quick brushing kiss. It seemed to burn through her every fibre. She gave a queer little cry.

'You will, won't you? You will?' he insisted softly.

5 'Nellie! *Nellie!* What ever are you so long for?' came Banford's faint cry from the outer darkness.

But he held her fast, and was murmuring with that intolerable softness and insistency:

'You will, won't you? Say yes! Say yes!'

10 March, who felt as if the fire had gone through her and scathed her, and as if she could do no more, murmured:

'Yes! Yes! Anything you like! Anything you like! Only let me go! Only let me go! Jill's calling.'

'You know you've promised,' he said insidiously.

15 'Yes! Yes! I do! –' Her voice suddenly rose into a shrill cry. 'All right, Jill, I'm coming.'

Startled, he let her go, and she went straight upstairs.

In the morning at breakfast, after he had looked round the place and attended to the stock and thought to himself that one could 20 live easily enough here, he said to Banford:

'Do you know what, Miss Banford?'

'Well, what?' said the good-natured, nervy Banford.

He looked at March, who was spreading jam on her bread.

'Shall I tell?' he said to her.

25 She looked up at him, and a deep pink colour flushed over her face.

'Yes, if you mean Jill,' she said. 'I hope you won't go talking all over the village, that's all.' And she swallowed her dry bread with difficulty.

30 'Whatever's coming?' said Banford, looking up with wide, tired, slightly reddened eyes. She was a thin, frail little thing, and her hair, which was delicate and thin, was bobbed, so it hung softly by her worn face in its faded brown and grey.

'Why, what do you think?' he said, smiling like one who has a 35 secret.

'How do I know!' said Banford.

'Can't you guess?' he said, making bright eyes, and smiling, pleased with himself.

'I'm sure I can't. What's more, I'm not going to try.'

'Nellie and I are going to be married.'

Banford put down her knife, out of her thin, delicate fingers, as if she would never take it up to eat any more. She stared with blank, reddened eyes.

'You what?' she exclaimed.

'We're going to get married. Aren't we, Nellie?' and he turned to March.

'You say so, anyway,' said March laconically. But again she flushed with an agonized flush. She, too, could swallow no more.

Banford looked at her like a bird that has been shot: a poor little sick bird. She gazed at her with all her wounded soul in her face, at the deep-flushed March.

'Never!' she exclaimed, helpless.

'It's quite right,' said the bright and gloating youth.

Banford turned aside her face, as if the sight of the food on the table made her sick. She sat like this for some moments, as if she were sick. Then, with one hand on the edge of the table, she rose to her feet.

'I'll *never* believe it, Nellie,' she cried. 'It's absolutely impossible!'

Her plaintive, fretful voice had a thread of hot anger and despair.

'Why? Why shouldn't you believe it?' asked the youth, with all his soft, velvety impertinence in his voice.

Banford looked at him from her wide vague eyes, as if he were some creature in a museum.

'Oh,' she said languidly, 'because she can never be such a fool. She can't lose her self-respect to such an extent.' Her voice was cold and plaintive, drifting.

'In what way will she lose her self-respect?' asked the boy.

Banford looked at him with vague fixity from behind her spectacles.

'If she hasn't lost it already,' she said.

He became very red, vermilion, under the slow vague stare from behind the spectacles.

'I don't see it at all,' he said.

'Probably you don't. I shouldn't expect you would,' said Banford, with that straying mild tone of remoteness which made her words even more insulting.

He sat stiff in his chair, staring with hot blue eyes from his scarlet face. An ugly look had come on his brow.

'My word, she doesn't know what she's letting herself in for,' said Banford, in her plaintive, drifting, insulting voice.

'What has it got to do with you, anyway?' said the youth in a temper.

'More than it has to do with you, probably,' she replied, plaintive and venomous.

'Oh, has it! I don't see that at all,' he jerked out.

'No, you wouldn't,' she answered, drifting.

'Anyhow,' said March, pushing back her hair and rising uncouthly, 'it's no good arguing about it.' And she seized the bread and the tea-pot, and strode away to the kitchen.

Banford let her fingers stray across her brow and along her hair, like one bemused. Then she turned and went away upstairs.

Henry sat stiff and sulky in his chair, with his face and his eyes on fire. March came and went, clearing the table. But Henry sat on, stiff with temper. He took no notice of her. She had regained her composure and her soft, even, creamy complexion. But her mouth was pursed up. She glanced at him each time as she came to take things from the table, glanced from her large, curious eyes, more in curiosity than anything. Such a long, red-faced sulky boy! That was all he was. He seemed as remote from her as if his red face were a red chimney-pot on a cottage across the fields, and she looked at him just as objectively, as remotely.

At length he got up and stalked out into the fields with the gun. He came in only at dinner-time, with the devil still in his face, but his manners quite polite. Nobody said anything particular: they sat each one at the sharp corner of a triangle, in obstinate remoteness. In the afternoon he went out again at once with the gun. He came in at nightfall with a rabbit and a pigeon. He stayed in all evening, but hardly opened his mouth. He was in the devil of a temper, feeling he had been insulted.

Banford's eyes were red, she had evidently been crying. But her manner was more remote and supercilious than ever, the way she turned her head if he spoke at all, as if he were some tramp or inferior intruder of that sort, made his blue eyes go almost black with rage. His face looked sulkier. But he never forgot his polite intonation, if he opened his mouth to speak.

March seemed to flourish in this atmosphere. She seemed to sit between the two antagonists with a little wicked smile on her face, enjoying herself. There was even a sort of complacency in the way she laboriously crocheted, this evening.

When he was in bed, the youth could hear the two women talking and arguing in their room. He sat up in bed and strained his ears to hear what they said. But he could hear nothing, it was too far off. Yet he could hear the soft, plaintive drip of Banford's voice, and March's deeper note.

The night was quiet, frosty. Big stars were snapping outside, beyond the ridge-tops of the pine-trees. He listened and listened. In the distance he heard a fox yelping: and the dogs from the farms barking in answer. But it was not that he wanted to hear. It was what the two women were saying.

He got stealthily out of bed, and stood by his door. He could hear no more than before. Very, very carefully he began to lift the door-latch. After quite a time he had his door open. Then he stepped stealthily out into the passage. The old oak planks were cold under his feet, and they creaked preposterously. He crept very, very gently up the one step, and along by the wall, till he stood outside their door. And there he held his breath and listened. Banford's voice:

'No, I simply couldn't stand it. I should be dead in a month. Which is just what he would be aiming at, of course. That would just be his game, to see me in the churchyard. No, Nellie, if you were to do such a thing as marry him, you could never stop here. I couldn't, I couldn't live in the same house with him. Oh – ! I feel quite sick with the smell of his clothes. And his red face simply turns me over. I can't eat my food when he's at the table. What a fool I was ever to let him stop. One ought *never* to try to do a kind action. It always flies back in your face like a boomerang.'

'Well, he's only got two more days,' said March.

'Yes, thank heaven. And when he's gone he'll never come in this house again. I feel so bad while he's here. And I know, I know he's only counting what he can get out of you. I *know* that's all it is.
5 He's just a good-for-nothing, who doesn't want to work, and who thinks he'll live on us. But he won't live on me. If you're such a fool, then it's your own lookout. Mrs Burgess knew him all the time he was here. And the old man could never get him to do any steady work. He was off with the gun on every occasion, just as he
10 is now. Nothing but the gun! Oh, I do hate it. You don't know what you're doing, Nellie, you don't. If you marry him he'll just make a fool of you. He'll go off and leave you stranded. I know he will, if he can't get Bailey Farm out of us – and he's not going to, while I live. While I live he's never going to set foot here. I know
15 what it would be. He'd soon think he was master of both of us, as he thinks he's master of you already.'

'But he isn't,' said Nellie.

'He thinks he is, anyway. And that's what he wants: to come and be master here. Yes, imagine it! That's what we've got the place
20 together for, is it, to be bossed and bullied by a hateful red-faced boy, a beastly labourer. Oh we *did* make a mistake when we let him stop. We ought never to have lowered ourselves. And I've had such a fight with all the people here, not to be pulled down to their level. No, he's not coming here. – And then you see – if he
25 can't have the place, he'll run off to Canada or somewhere again, as if he'd never known you. And here you'll be, absolutely ruined and made a fool of. I know I shall never have any peace of mind again.'

'We'll tell him he can't come here. We'll tell him that,' said
30 March.

'Oh, don't you bother, I'm going to tell him that, and other things as well, before he goes. He's not going to have all his own way, while I've got the strength left to speak. Oh, Nellie, he'll despise you, he'll despise you like the awful little beast he is, if you
35 give way to him. I'd no more trust him than I'd trust a cat not to steal. He's deep, he's deep, and he's bossy, and he's selfish through

and through, as cold as ice. All he wants is to make use of you. And when you're no more use to him, then I pity you.'

'I don't think he's as bad as all that,' said March.

'No, because he's been playing up to you. But you'll find out, if you see much more of him. Oh, Nellie, I can't bear to think of it.'

'Well, it won't hurt you, Jill darling.'

'Won't it! Won't it! I shall never know a moment's peace again while I live, nor a moment's happiness. No, Nellie –' and Banford began to weep bitterly.

The boy outside could hear the stifled sound of the woman's sobbing, and could hear March's soft, deep, tender voice comforting, with wonderful gentleness and tenderness, the weeping woman.

His eyes were so round and wide that he seemed to see the whole night, and his ears were almost jumping off his head. He was frozen stiff. He crept back to bed, but felt as if the top of his head were coming off. He could not sleep. He could not keep still. He rose, quietly dressed himself, and crept out on to the landing once more. The women were silent. He went softly downstairs and out to the kitchen.

Then he put on his boots and overcoat, and took the gun. He did not think to go away from the farm. No, he only took the gun. As softly as possible he unfastened the door and went out into the frosty December night. The air was still, the stars bright, the pine-trees seemed to bristle audibly in the sky. He went stealthily away down a fence-side, looking for something to shoot. At the same time he remembered that he ought not to shoot and frighten the women.

So he prowled round the edge of the gorse cover, and through the grove of tall old hollies, to the woodside. There he skirted the fence, peering through the darkness with dilated eyes that seemed to be able to grow black and full of sight in the dark, like a cat's. An owl was slowly and mournfully whooing round a great oak tree. He stepped stealthily with his gun, listening, listening, watching.

As he stood under the oaks of the wood-edge he heard the dogs from the neighbouring cottage, up the hill, yelling suddenly and

startlingly, and the wakened dogs from the farms around barking answer. And suddenly, it seemed to him England was little and tight, he felt the landscape was constricted even in the dark, and that there were too many dogs in the night, making a noise like a
5 fence of sound, like the network of English hedges netting the view. He felt the fox didn't have a chance. For it must be the fox that had started all this hullabaloo.

Why not watch for him, anyhow! He would no doubt be coming sniffing round. The lad walked downhill to where the farmstead
10 with its few pine-trees crouched blackly. In the angle of the long shed, in the black dark, he crouched down. He knew the fox would be coming. It seemed to him it would be the last of the foxes in this loudly-barking, thick-voiced England, tight with innumerable little houses.

15 He sat a long time with his eyes fixed unchanging upon the open gateway, where a little light seemed to fall from the stars or from the horizon, who knows. He was sitting on a log in a dark corner with the gun across his knees. The pine-trees snapped. Once a chicken fell off its perch in the barn, with a loud crawk and cackle
20 and commotion that startled him, and he stood up, watching with all his eyes, thinking it might be a rat. But he *felt* it was nothing. So he sat down again with the gun on his knees and his hands tucked in to keep them warm, and his eyes fixed unblinking on the pale reach of the open gateway. He felt he could smell the hot, sickly,
25 rich smell of live chickens on the cold air.

And then – a shadow. A sliding shadow in the gateway. He gathered all his vision into a concentrated spark, and saw the shadow of the fox, the fox creeping on his belly through the gate. There he went, on his belly like a snake. The boy smiled to himself
30 and brought the gun to his shoulder. He knew quite well what would happen. He knew the fox would go to where the fowl-door was boarded up, and sniff there. He knew he would lie there for a minute, sniffing the fowls within. And then he would start again prowling under the edge of the old barn, waiting to get in.

35 The fowl-door was at the top of a slight incline. Soft, soft as a shadow the fox slid up this incline, and crouched with his nose to

the boards. And at the same moment there was the awful crash of a gun reverberating between the old buildings, as if all the night had gone smash. But the boy watched keenly. He saw even the white belly of the fox as the beast beat his paws in death. So he went forward. 5

There was a commotion everywhere. The fowls were scuffling and crawking, the ducks were quark-quarking, the pony had stamped wildly to his feet. But the fox was on his side, struggling in his last tremors. The boy bent over him and smelt his foxy smell.

There was a sound of a window opening upstairs, then March's 10 voice calling:

'Who is it?'

'It's me,' said Henry; 'I've shot the fox.'

'Oh, goodness! You nearly frightened us to death.'

'Did I? I'm awfully sorry.' 15

'Whatever made you get up?'

'I heard him about.'

'And have you shot him?'

'Yes, he's here,' and the boy stood in the yard holding up the warm, dead brute. 'You can't see, can you? Wait a minute.' And 20 he took his flash-light from his pocket, and flashed it on to the dead animal. He was holding it by the brush. March saw, in the middle of the darkness, just the reddish fleece and the white belly and the white underneath of the pointed chin, and the queer, dangling paws. She did not know what to say. 25

'He's a beauty,' he said. 'He will make you a lovely fur.'

'You don't catch me wearing a fox fur,' she replied.

'Oh!' he said. And he switched off the light.

'Well, I should think you'll come in and go to bed again now,' she said. 30

'Probably I shall. What time is it?'

'What time is it, Jill?' called March's voice. It was a quarter to one.

That night March had another dream. She dreamed that Banford was dead, and that she, March, was sobbing her heart out. Then 35 she had to put Banford into her coffin. And the coffin was the

rough wood-box in which the bits of chopped wood were kept in the kitchen, by the fire. This was the coffin, and there was no other, and March was in agony and dazed bewilderment, looking for something to line the box with, something to make it soft with,
5 something to cover up the poor dead darling. Because she couldn't lay her in there just in her white thin nightdress, in the horrible wood-box. So she hunted and hunted, and picked up thing after thing, and threw it aside in the agony of dream-frustration. And in her dream-despair all she could find that would do was a fox-skin.
10 She knew that it wasn't right, that this was not what she could have. But it was all she could find. And so she folded the brush of the fox, and laid her darling Jill's head on this, and she brought round the skin of the fox and laid it on the top of the body, so that it seemed to make a whole ruddy, fiery coverlet, and she cried and
15 cried and woke to find the tears streaming down her face.

The first thing that both she and Banford did in the morning was to go out to see the fox. He had hung it up by the heels in the shed, with its poor brush falling backwards. It was a lovely dog-fox in its prime with a handsome thick winter coat: a lovely golden-red
20 colour, with grey as it passed to the belly, and belly all white, and a great full brush with a delicate black and grey and pure white tip.

'Poor brute!' said Banford. 'If it wasn't such a thieving wretch, you'd feel sorry for it.'

March said nothing, but stood with her foot trailing aside, one hip
25 out; her face was pale and her eyes big and black, watching the dead animal that was suspended upside down. White and soft as snow his belly: white and soft as snow. She passed her hand softly down it. And his wonderful black-glinted brush was full and frictional, wonderful. She passed her hand down this also, and quivered.
30 Time after time she took the full fur of that thick tail between her hand and passed her hand slowly downwards. Wonderful sharp thick splendour of a tail! And he was dead! She pursed her lips, and her eyes went black and vacant. Then she took the head in her hand.

35 Henry was sauntering up, so Banford walked rather pointedly away. March stood there bemused, with the head of the fox in her

hand. She was wondering, wondering, wondering over his long fine muzzle. For some reason it reminded her of a spoon or a spatula. She felt she could not understand it. The beast was a strange beast to her, incomprehensible, out of her range. Wonderful silver whiskers he had, like ice-threads. And pricked ears with hair inside. – But that long, long slender spoon of a nose! – and the marvellous white teeth beneath! It was to thrust forward and bite with, deep, deep into the living prey, to bite and bite the blood.

'He's a beauty, isn't he?' said Henry, standing by.

'Oh yes, he's a fine big fox. I wonder how many chickens he's responsible for,' she replied.

'A good many. Do you think he's the same one you saw in the summer?'

'I should think very likely he is,' she replied.

He watched her, but he could make nothing of her. Partly she was so shy and virgin, and partly she was so grim, matter-of-fact, shrewish. What she said seemed to him so different from the look of her big, queer dark eyes.

'Are you going to skin him?' she asked.

'Yes, when I've had breakfast, and got a board to peg him on.'

'My word, what a strong smell he's got! Pooo! – It'll take some washing off one's hands. I don't know why I was so silly as to handle him.' – And she looked at her right hand, that had passed down his belly and along his tail, and had even got a tiny streak of blood from one dark place in his fur.

'Have you seen the chickens when they smell him, how frightened they are?' he said.

'Yes, aren't they!'

'You must mind you don't get some of his fleas.'

'Oh, fleas!' she replied, nonchalant.

Later in the day she saw the fox's skin nailed flat on a board, as if crucified. It gave her an uneasy feeling.

The boy was angry. He went about with his mouth shut, as if he had swallowed part of his chin. But in behaviour he was polite and affable. He did not say anything about his intention. And he left March alone.

That evening they sat in the dining-room. Banford wouldn't have him in her sitting-room any more. There was a very big log on the fire. And everybody was busy. Banford had letters to write, March was sewing a dress, and he was mending some little contrivance.

Banford stopped her letter-writing from time to time to look round and rest her eyes. The boy had his head down, his face hidden over his job.

'Let's see,' said Banford. 'What train do you go by, Henry?'

He looked up straight at her.

'The morning train. In the morning,' he said.

'What, the eight-ten or the eleven-twenty?'

'The eleven-twenty, I suppose,' he said.

'That is the day after tomorrow?' said Banford.

'Yes, the day after tomorrow.'

'Mmm!' murmured Banford, and she returned to her writing. But as she was licking her envelope, she asked:

'And what plans have you made for the future, if I may ask?'

'Plans?' he said, his face very bright and angry.

'I mean about you and Nellie, if you are going on with this business. When do you expect the wedding to come off?' She spoke in a jeering tone.

'Oh, the wedding!' he replied. 'I don't know.'

'Don't you know anything?' said Banford. 'Are you going to clear out on Friday and leave things no more settled than they are?'

'Well, why shouldn't I? We can always write letters.'

'Yes, of course you can. But I wanted to know because of this place. If Nellie is going to get married all of a sudden, I shall have to be looking round for a new partner.'

'Couldn't she stay on here if she was married?' he said. He knew quite well what was coming.

'Oh,' said Banford, 'this is no place for a married couple. There's not enough work to keep a man going, for one thing. And there's no money to be made. It's quite useless your thinking of staying on here if you marry. Absolutely!'

'Yes, but I wasn't thinking of staying on here,' he said.

'Well, that's what I want to know. And what about Nellie, then?
How long is *she* going to be here with me, in that case?'

The two antagonists looked at one another.

'That I can't say,' he answered.

'Oh, go along,' she cried petulantly. 'You must have some idea
what you are going to do, if you ask a woman to marry you. Unless
it's all a hoax.'

'Why should it be a hoax? – I am going back to Canada.'

'And taking her with you?'

'Yes, certainly.'

'You hear that, Nellie?' said Banford.

March, who had had her head bent over her sewing, now looked
up with a sharp pink blush on her face and a queer, sardonic laugh
in her eyes and on her twisted mouth.

'That's the first time I've heard that I was going to Canada,' she
said.

'Well, you have to hear it for the first time, haven't you?' said
the boy.

'Yes, I suppose I have,' she said nonchalantly. And she went
back to her sewing.

'You're quite ready, are you, to go to Canada? Are you, Nellie?'
asked Banford.

March looked up again. She let her shoulders go slack, and let
her hand that held the needle lie loose in her lap.

'It depends on *how* I'm going,' she said. 'I don't think I want to
go jammed up in the steerage, as a soldier's wife. I'm afraid I'm
not used to that way.'

The boy watched her with bright eyes.

'Would you rather stay over here while I go first?' he asked.

'I would, if that's the only alternative,' she replied.

'That's much the wisest. Don't make it any fixed engagement,'
said Banford. 'Leave yourself free to go or not after he's got back
and found you a place, Nellie. Anything else is madness, madness.'

'Don't you think,' said the youth, 'we ought to get married
before I go – and then go together, or separate, according to how
it happens?'

'I think it's a *terrible* idea,' cried Banford.

But the boy was watching March.

'What do you think?' he asked her.

She let her eyes stray vaguely into space.

5   'Well, I don't know,' she said. 'I shall have to think about it.'

'Why?' he asked, pertinently.

'Why?' – She repeated his question in a mocking way and looked at him laughing, though her face was pink again. 'I should think there's plenty of reasons why.'

10   He watched her in silence. She seemed to have escaped him. She had got into league with Banford against him. There was again the queer sardonic look about her; she would mock stoically at everything he said or which life offered.

'Of course,' he said, 'I don't want to press you to do anything

15 you don't wish to do.'

'I should think not, indeed,' cried Banford indignantly.

At bedtime Banford said plaintively to March:

'You take my hot bottle up for me, Nellie, will you?'

'Yes, I'll do it,' said March, with the kind of willing unwillingness

20 she so often showed towards her beloved but uncertain Jill.

The two women went upstairs. After a time March called from the top of the stairs: 'Good-night, Henry. I shan't be coming down. You'll see to the lamp and the fire, won't you?'

The next day Henry went about with the cloud on his brow and

25 his young cub's face shut up tight. He was cogitating all the time. He had wanted March to marry him and go back to Canada with him. And he had been sure she would do it. Why he wanted her he didn't know. But he did want her. He had set his mind on her. And he was convulsed with a youth's fury at being thwarted. To be

30 thwarted, to be thwarted! It made him so furious inside, that he did not know what to do with himself. But he kept himself in hand. Because even now things might turn out differently. She might come over to him. Of course she might. It was her business to do so.

35   Things drew to a tension again towards evening. He and Banford had avoided each other all day. In fact Banford went in to the little

town by the 11.20 train. It was market day. She arrived back on the 4.25. Just as the night was falling Henry saw her little figure in a dark-blue coat and a dark-blue tam-o'-shanter hat crossing the first meadow from the station. He stood under one of the wild pear trees, with the old dead leaves round his feet. And he watched the little blue figure advancing persistently over the rough winter-ragged meadow. She had her arms full of parcels, and advanced slowly, frail thing she was, but with that devilish little certainty which he so detested in her. He stood invisible under the pear-tree, watching her every step. And if looks could have affected her, she would have felt a log of iron on each of her ankles as she made her way forward. 'You're a nasty little thing, you are,' he was saying softly, across the distance. 'You're a nasty little thing. I hope you'll be paid back for all the harm you've done me for nothing. I hope you will – you nasty little thing. I hope you'll have to pay for it. You will, if wishes are anything. You nasty little creature that you are.'

She was toiling slowly up the slope. But if she had been slipping back at every step towards the Bottomless Pit, he would not have gone to help her with her parcels. Aha, there went March, striding with her long land stride in her breeches and her short tunic! Striding downhill at a great pace, and even running a few steps now and then, in her great solicitude and desire to come to the rescue of the little Banford. The boy watched her with rage in his heart. See her leap a ditch, and run, run as if a house was on fire, just to get to that creeping dark little object down there! So, the Banford just stood still and waited. And March strode up and took *all* the parcels except a bunch of yellow chrysanthemums. These the Banford still carried – yellow chrysanthemums!

'Yes, you look well, don't you,' he said softly into the dusk air. 'You look well, pottering up there with a bunch of flowers, you do. I'd make you eat them for your tea, if you hug them so tight. And I'd give them you for breakfast again, I would. I'd give you flowers. Nothing but flowers.'

He watched the progress of the two women. He could hear their voices: March always outspoken and rather scolding in her tenderness, Banford murmuring rather vaguely. They were evidently good friends. He could not hear what they said till they came to the fence of the home meadow, which they must climb. Then he saw March manfully climbing over the bars with all her packages in her arms, and on the still air he heard Banford's fretful:

'Why don't you let me help you with the parcels?' She had a queer plaintive hitch in her voice. – Then came March's robust and reckless:

'Oh, I can manage. Don't you bother about me. You've all you can do to get yourself over.'

'Yes, that's all very well,' said Banford fretfully. 'You say *Don't you bother about me*, and then all the while you feel injured because nobody thinks of you.'

'When do I feel injured?' said March.

'Always. You always feel injured. Now you're feeling injured because I won't have that boy to come and live on the farm.'

'I'm not feeling injured at all,' said March.

'I know you are. When he's gone you'll sulk over it. I know you will.'

'Shall I?' said March. 'We'll see.'

'Yes, we *shall* see, unfortunately. – I can't think how you can make yourself so cheap. I can't *imagine* how you can lower yourself like it.'

'I haven't lowered myself,' said March.

'I don't know what you call it, then. Letting a boy like that come so cheeky and impudent and make a mug of you. I don't know what you think of yourself. How much respect do you think he's going to have for you afterwards? – My word, I wouldn't be in your shoes, if you married him.'

'Of course you wouldn't. My boots are a good bit too big for you, and not half dainty enough,' said March, with rather a misfire sarcasm.

'I thought you had too much pride, really I did. A woman's got to hold herself high, especially with a youth like that. Why, he's impudent. Even the way he forced himself on us at the start.'

'We asked him to stay,' said March.

'Not till he'd almost forced us to. – And then he's so cocky and self-assured. My word, he puts my back up. I simply can't imagine how you can let him treat you so cheaply.'

'I don't let him treat me cheaply,' said March. 'Don't you worry yourself, nobody's going to treat me cheaply. And even you aren't,   5
either.' She had a tender defiance, and a certain fire in her voice.

'Yes, it's sure to come back to me,' said Banford bitterly. 'That's always the end of it. I believe you only do it to spite me.'

They went now in silence up the steep grassy slope and over the brow through the gorse-bushes. On the other side of the hedge the   10
boy followed in the dusk, at some little distance. Now and then, through the huge ancient hedge of hawthorn, risen into trees, he saw the two dark figures creeping up the hill. As he came to the top of the slope he saw the homestead dark in the twilight, with a huge old pear-tree leaning from the near gable, and a little yellow   15
light twinkling in the small side windows of the kitchen. He heard the clink of the latch and saw the kitchen door open into light as the two women went indoors. So, they were at home.

And so! – this was what they thought of him. It was rather in his nature to be a listener, so he was not at all surprised whatever   20
he heard. The things people said about him always missed him personally. He was only rather surprised at the women's way with one another. And he disliked the Banford with an acid dislike. And he felt drawn to the March again. He felt again irresistibly drawn to her. He felt there was a secret bond, a secret thread between   25
him and her, something very exclusive, which shut out everybody else and made him and her possess each other in secret.

He hoped again that she would have him. He hoped with his blood suddenly firing up that she would agree to marry him quite quickly: at Christmas, very likely. Christmas was not far off. He   30
wanted, whatever else happened, to snatch her into a hasty marriage and a consummation with him. Then for the future, they could arrange later. But he hoped it would happen as he wanted it. He hoped that tonight she would stay a little while with him, after Banford had gone upstairs. He hoped he could touch her soft,   35
creamy cheek, her strange, frightened face. He hoped he could

look into her dilated, frightened dark eyes, quite near. He hoped
he might even put his hand on her bosom and feel her soft breasts
under her tunic. His heart beat deep and powerful as he thought
of that. He wanted very much to do so. He wanted to make sure
5 of her soft woman's breasts under her tunic. She always kept the
brown linen coat buttoned so close up to her throat. It seemed to
him like some perilous secret, that her soft woman's breasts must
be buttoned up in that uniform. It seemed to him moreover that
they were so much softer, tenderer, more lovely and lovable, shut
10 up in that tunic, than were the Banford's breasts, under her soft
blouses and chiffon dresses. The Banford would have little iron
breasts, he said to himself. For all her frailty and fretfulness and
delicacy, she would have tiny iron breasts. But March, under her
crude, fast, workman's tunic, would have soft white breasts, white
15 and unseen. So he told himself, and his blood burned.

When he went in to tea, he had a surprise. He appeared at the
inner door, his face very ruddy and vivid and his blue eyes shining,
dropping his head forward as he came in, in his usual way, and
hesitating in the doorway to watch the inside of the room, keenly
20 and cautiously, before he entered. He was wearing a long-sleeved
waistcoat. His face seemed extraordinarily a piece of the out-of-
doors come indoors: as holly-berries do. In his second of pause in
the doorway he took in the two women sitting at table, at opposite
ends, saw them sharply. And to his amazement March was dressed
25 in a dress of dull, green silk crape. His mouth came open in surprise.
If she had suddenly grown a moustache he could not have been
more surprised.

'Why,' he said, 'do you wear a dress, then?'

She looked up, flushing a deep rose colour, and twisting her
30 mouth with a smile, said:

'Of course I do. What else do you expect me to wear, but a
dress?'

'A land girl's uniform, of course,' said he.

'Oh,' she cried nonchalant, 'that's only for this dirty mucky work
35 about here.'

'Isn't it your proper dress, then?' he said.

'No, not indoors it isn't,' she said. But she was blushing all the time as she poured out his tea. He sat down in his chair at table, unable to take his eyes off her. Her dress was a perfectly simple slip of bluey-green crape, with a line of gold stitching round the top and round the sleeves, which came to the elbow. It was cut just plain, and round at the top, and showed her white soft throat. Her arms he knew, strong and firm muscled, for he had often seen her with her sleeves rolled up. But he looked her up and down, up and down.

Banford, at the other end of the table, said not a word, but piggled with the sardine on her plate. He had forgotten her existence. He just simply stared at March, while he ate his bread and margarine in huge mouthfuls, forgetting even his tea.

'Well, I never knew anything make such a difference!' he murmured, across his mouthfuls.

'Oh, goodness!' cried March, blushing still more. 'I might be a pink monkey!'

And she rose quickly to her feet and took the tea-pot to the fire, to the kettle. And as she crouched on the hearth with her green slip about her, the boy stared more wide-eyed than ever. Through the crape her woman's form seemed soft and womanly. And when she stood up and walked he saw her legs move soft within her moderately short skirt. She had on black silk stockings and small patent shoes with little gold buckles.

No, she was another being. She was something quite different. Seeing her always in the hard-cloth breeches, wide on the hips, buttoned on the knee, strong as armour, and in the brown puttees and thick boots, it had never occurred to him that she had a woman's legs and feet. Now it came upon him. She had a woman's soft, skirted legs, and she was accessible. He blushed to the roots of his hair, shoved his nose in his teacup and drank his tea with a little noise that made Banford simply squirm: and strangely, suddenly he felt a man, no longer a youth. He felt a man, with all a man's grave weight of responsibility. A curious quietness and gravity came over his soul. He felt a man, quiet, with a little of the heaviness of male destiny upon him.

She was soft and accessible in her dress. The thought went home in him like an everlasting responsibility.

'Oh for goodness' sake, say something, somebody,' cried Banford fretfully. 'It might be a funeral.' The boy looked at her, and she could not bear his face.

'A funeral!' said March, with a twisted smile. 'Why, that breaks my dream.'

Suddenly she had thought of Banford in the wood-box for a coffin.

'What, have you been dreaming of a wedding?' said Banford sarcastically.

'Must have been,' said March.

'Whose wedding?' asked the boy.

'I can't remember,' said March.

She was shy and rather awkward that evening, in spite of the fact that, wearing a dress, her bearing was much more subdued than in her uniform. She felt unpeeled and rather exposed. She felt almost improper.

They talked desultorily about Henry's departure next morning, and made the trivial arrangement. But of the matter on their minds, none of them spoke. They were rather quiet and friendly this evening; Banford had practically nothing to say. But inside herself she seemed still, perhaps kindly.

At nine o'clock March brought in the tray with the everlasting tea and a little cold meat which Banford had managed to procure. It was the last supper, so Banford did not want to be disagreeable. She felt a bit sorry for the boy, and felt she must be as nice as she could.

He wanted her to go to bed. She was usually the first. But she sat on in her chair under the lamp, glancing at her book now and then, and staring into the fire. A deep silence had come into the room. It was broken by March asking, in a rather small tone:

'What time is it, Jill?'

'Five past ten,' said Banford, looking at her wrist.

And then not a sound. The boy had looked up from the book he was holding between his knees. His rather wide, cat-shaped face had its obstinate look, his eyes were watchful.

'What about bed?' said March at last.

'I'm ready when you are,' said Banford.

'Oh, very well,' said March. 'I'll fill your bottle.'

She was as good as her word. When the hot-water bottle was ready, she lit a candle and went upstairs with it. Banford remained in her chair, listening acutely. March came downstairs again.

'There you are then,' she said. 'Are you going up?'

'Yes, in a minute,' said Banford. But the minute passed, and she sat on in her chair under the lamp.

Henry, whose eyes were shining like a cat's as he watched from under his brows, and whose face seemed wider, more chubbed and cat-like with unalterable obstinacy, now rose to his feet to try his throw.

'I think I'll go and look if I can see the she-fox,' he said. 'She may be creeping round. Won't you come as well for a minute, Nellie, and see if we see anything?'

'Me!' cried March, looking up with her startled, wondering face.

'Yes. Come on,' he said. It was wonderful how soft and warm and coaxing his voice could be, how near. The very sound of it made Banford's blood boil. 'Come on for a minute,' he said, looking down into her uplifted, unsure face.

And she rose to her feet as if drawn up by this young, ruddy face that was looking down on her.

'I should think you're never going out at this time of night, Nellie!' cried Banford.

'Yes, just for a minute,' said the boy, looking round on her, and speaking with an odd sharp yelp in his voice.

March looked from one to the other, as if confused, vague. Banford rose to her feet for battle.

'Why, it's ridiculous. It's bitter cold. You'll catch your death in that thin frock. And in those slippers. You're not going to do any such thing.'

There was a moment's pause. Banford turtled up like a little fighting cock, facing March and the boy.

'Oh, I don't think you need worry yourself,' he replied. 'A

moment under the stars won't do anybody any damage. I'll get the rug off the sofa in the dining-room. You're coming, Nellie.'

His voice had so much anger and contempt and fury in it as he spoke to Banford: and so much tenderness and proud authority as
5 he spoke to March, that the latter answered:

'Yes, I'm coming.'

And she turned with him to the door.

Banford, standing there in the middle of the room, suddenly burst into a long wail and a spasm of sobs. She covered her face
10 with her poor thin hands, and her thin shoulders shook in an agony of weeping. March looked back from the door.

'Jill!' she cried in a frantic tone, like someone just coming awake. And she seemed to start towards her darling.

But the boy had March's arm in his grip, and she could not
15 move. She did not know why she could not move. It was as in a dream when the heart strains and the body cannot stir.

'Never mind,' said the boy softly. 'Let her cry. Let her cry. She will have to cry sooner or later. And the tears will relieve her feelings. They will do her good.'

20 So he drew March slowly through the doorway. But her last look was back to the poor little figure which stood in the middle of the room with covered face and thin shoulders shaken with bitter weeping.

In the dining-room he picked up the rug and said:

'Wrap yourself up in this.'

25 She obeyed – and they reached the kitchen door, he holding her soft and firm by the arm, though she did not know it. When she saw the night outside she started back.

'I must go back to Jill,' she said. 'I *must*! Oh yes, I must.'

Her tone sounded final. The boy let go of her and she turned
30 indoors. But he seized her again and arrested her.

'Wait a minute,' he said. 'Wait a minute. Even if you go you're not going yet.'

'Leave go! Leave go!' she cried. 'My place is at Jill's side. Poor little thing, she's sobbing her heart out.'

35 'Yes,' said the boy bitterly. 'And your heart too, and mine as well.'

'Your heart?' said March. He still gripped her and detained her. 'Isn't it as good as her heart?' he said. 'Or do you think it's not?'

'Your heart?' she said again, incredulous.

'Yes, mine! Mine! Do you think I haven't *got* a heart?' – And with his hot grasp he took her hand and pressed it under his left breast. 'There's my heart,' he said, 'if you don't believe in it.'

It was wonder which made her attend. And then she felt the deep, heavy, powerful stroke of his heart, terrible, like something from beyond. It was like something from beyond, something awful from outside, signalling to her. And the signal paralysed her. It beat upon her very soul, and made her helpless. She forgot Jill. She could not think of Jill any more. She could not think of her. That terrible signalling from outside!

The boy put his arm round her waist.

'Come with me,' he said gently. 'Come and let us say what we've got to say.'

And he drew her outside, closed the door. And she went with him darkly down the garden path. That he should have a beating heart! And that he should have his arm round her, outside the blanket! She was too confused to think who he was or what he was.

He took her to a dark corner of the shed, where there was a tool-box with a lid, long and low.

'We'll sit here a minute,' he said.

And obediently she sat down by his side.

'Give me your hand,' he said.

She gave him both her hands, and he held them between his own. He was young, and it made him tremble.

'You'll marry me. You'll marry me before I go back, won't you?' he pleaded.

'Why, aren't we both a pair of fools?' she said.

He had put her in the corner, so that she should not look out and see the lighted window of the house, across the dark garden. He tried to keep her all there inside the shed with him.

'In what way a pair of fools?' he said. 'If you go back to Canada with me, I've got a job and a good wage waiting for me, and it's a nice place, near the mountains. Why shouldn't you marry me?

Why shouldn't we marry? I should like to have you there with me. I should like to feel I'd got somebody there, at the back of me, all my life.'

'You'd easily find somebody else, who'd suit you better,' she
5 said.

'Yes, I might easily find another girl. I know I could. But not one I really wanted. I've never met one I really wanted, for good. You see, I'm thinking of all my life. If I marry, I want to feel it's for all my life. Other girls: well, they're just girls, nice enough to
10 go a walk with now and then. Nice enough for a bit of play. But when I think of my life, then I should be very sorry to have to marry one of them, I should indeed.'

'You mean they wouldn't make you a good wife.'

'Yes, I mean that. But I don't mean they wouldn't do their duty
15 by me. I mean – I don't know what I mean. Only when I think of my life, and of you, then the two things go together.'

'And what if they didn't?' she said, with her odd sardonic touch.

'Well, I think they would.'

They sat for some time silent. He held her hands in his, but he
20 did not make love to her. Since he had realized that she was a woman, and vulnerable, accessible, a certain heaviness had possessed his soul. He did not want to make love to her. He shrank from any such performance, almost with fear. She was a woman, and vulnerable, accessible to him finally, and he held back from
25 that which was ahead, almost with dread. It was a kind of darkness he knew he would enter finally, but of which he did not want as yet even to think. She was the woman, and he was responsible for the strange vulnerability he had suddenly realized in her.

'No,' she said at last, 'I'm a fool. I know I'm a fool.'
30 'What for?' he asked.

'To go on with this business.'

'Do you mean me?' he asked.

'No, I mean myself. I'm making a fool of myself, and a big one.'

'Why, because you don't want to marry me, really?'
35 'Oh, I don't know whether I'm against it, as a matter of fact. That's just it. I don't know.'

He looked at her in the darkness, puzzled. He did not in the least know what she meant.

'And don't you know whether you like to sit here with me this minute, or not?' he asked.

'No, I don't, really. I don't know whether I wish I was somewhere else, or whether I like being here. I don't know, really.'

'Do you wish you were with Miss Banford? Do you wish you'd gone to bed with her?' he asked, as a challenge.

She waited a long time before she answered:

'No,' she said at last. 'I don't wish that.'

'And do you think you would spend all your life with her – when your hair goes white, and you are old?' he said.

'No,' she said, without much hesitation. 'I don't see Jill and me two old women together.'

'And don't you think, when I'm an old man, and you're an old woman, we might be together still, as we are now?' he said.

'Well, not as we are now,' she replied. 'But I could imagine – no, I can't. I can't imagine you an old man. Besides, it's dreadful!'

'What, to be an old man?'

'Yes, of course.'

'Not when the time comes,' he said. 'But it hasn't come. Only it will. And when it does, I should like to think you'd be there as well.'

'Sort of old age pensions,' she said dryly.

Her kind of witless humour always startled him. He never knew what she meant. Probably she didn't quite know herself.

'No,' he said, hurt.

'I don't know why you harp on old age,' she said. 'I'm not ninety.'

'Did anybody ever say you were?' he asked, offended.

They were silent for some time, pulling different ways in the silence.

'I don't want you to make fun of me,' he said.

'Don't you?' she replied, enigmatic.

'No, because just this minute I'm serious. And when I'm serious, I believe in not making fun of it.'

'You mean nobody else can make fun of you,' she replied.

'Yes, I mean that. And I mean I don't believe in making fun of it myself. When it comes over me so that I'm serious, then – there it is, I don't want it to be laughed at.'

5 She was silent for some time. Then she said, in a vague, almost pained voice:

'No, I'm not laughing at you.'

A hot wave rose in his heart.

'You believe me, do you?' he asked.

10 'Yes, I believe you,' she replied, with a twang of her old tired nonchalance, as if she gave in because she was tired. – But he didn't care. His heart was hot and clamorous.

'So you agree to marry me before I go? – perhaps at Christmas?'

'Yes, I agree.'

15 'There!' he exclaimed. 'That's settled it.'

And he sat silent, unconscious, with all the blood burning in all his veins, like fire in all the branches and twigs of him. He only pressed her two hands to his chest, without knowing. When the curious passion began to die down, he seemed to come awake to

20 the world.

'We'll go in, shall we?' he said: as if he realized it was cold.

She rose without answering.

'Kiss me before we go, now you've said it,' he said.

And he kissed her gently on the mouth, with a young, frightened

25 kiss. It made her feel so young, too, and frightened, and wondering: and tired, tired, as if she were going to sleep.

They went indoors. And in the sitting-room, there, crouched by the fire like a queer little witch, was Banford. She looked round with reddened eyes as they entered, but did not rise. He thought

30 she looked frightening, unnatural, crouching there and looking round at them. Evil he thought her look was, and he crossed his fingers.

Banford saw the ruddy, elate face of the youth: he seemed strangely tall and bright and looming. And March had a delicate

35 look on her face, she wanted to hide her face, to screen it, to let it not be seen.

'You've come at last,' said Banford uglily.

'Yes, we've come,' said he.

'You've been long enough for anything,' she said.

'Yes, we have. We've settled it. We shall marry as soon as possible,' he replied.

'Oh, you've settled it, have you! Well, I hope you won't live to repent it,' said Banford.

'I hope so too,' he replied.

'Are you going to bed *now*, Nellie?' said Banford.

'Yes, I'm going now.'

'Then for goodness' sake come along.'

March looked at the boy. He was glancing with his very bright eyes at her and at Banford. March looked at him wistfully. She wished she could stay with him. She wished she had married him already, and it was all over. For oh, she felt suddenly so safe with him. She felt so strangely safe and peaceful in his presence. If only she could sleep in his shelter, and not with Jill. She felt afraid of Jill. In her dim, tender state, it was agony to have to go with Jill and sleep with her. She wanted the boy to save her. She looked again at him.

And he, watching with bright eyes, divined something of what she felt. It puzzled and distressed him that she must go with Jill.

'I shan't forget what you've promised,' he said, looking clear into her eyes, right into her eyes, so that he seemed to occupy all herself with his queer, bright look.

She smiled to him, faintly, gently. She felt safe again – safe with him.

But in spite of all the boy's precautions, he had a set-back. The morning he was leaving the farm he got March to accompany him to the market-town, about six miles away, where they went to the registrar and had their names stuck up as two people who were going to marry. He was to come at Christmas, and the wedding was to take place then. He hoped in the spring to be able to take March back to Canada with him, now the war was really over. Though he was so young, he had saved some money.

'You never have to be without *some* money at the back of you, if you can help it,' he said.

So she saw him off in the train that was going West: his camp was on Salisbury plains. And with big dark eyes she watched him go, and it seemed as if everything real in life was retreating as the train retreated with his queer, chubby, ruddy face, that seemed so
5 broad across the cheeks, and which never seemed to change its expression, save when a cloud of sulky anger hung on the brow, or the bright eyes fixed themselves in their stare. This was what happened now. He leaned there out of the carriage window as the train drew off, saying good-bye and staring back at her, but his face
10 quite unchanged. There was no emotion on his face. Only his eyes tightened and became fixed and intent in their watching, as a cat when suddenly she sees something and stares. So the boy's eyes stared fixedly as the train drew away, and she was left feeling intensely forlorn. Failing his physical presence, she seemed to have
15 nothing of him. And she had nothing of anything. Only his face was fixed in her mind: the full, ruddy, unchanging cheeks, and the straight snout of a nose, and the two eyes staring above. All she could remember was how he suddenly wrinkled his nose when he laughed, as a puppy does when he is playfully growling. But him,
20 himself, and what he was – she knew nothing, she had nothing of him when he left her.

On the ninth day after he had left her he received this letter.

'Dear Henry,

I have been over it all again in my mind, this business of me and you,
25 and it seems to me impossible. When you aren't there I see what a fool I am. When you are there you seem to blind me to things as they actually are. You make me see things all unreal and I don't know what. Then when I am alone again with Jill I seem to come to my own senses and realize what a fool I am making of myself and how I am treating you unfairly.
30 Because it must be unfair to you for me to go on with this affair when I can't feel in my heart that I really love you. I know people talk a lot of stuff and nonsense about love, and I don't want to do that. I want to keep to plain facts and act in a sensible way. And that seems to me what I'm not doing. I don't see on what grounds I am going to marry you. I know I am
35 not head over heels in love with you, as I have fancied myself to be with

fellows when I was a young fool of a girl. You are an absolute stranger to me, and it seems to me you will always be one. So on what grounds am I going to marry you? When I think of Jill she is ten times more real to me. I know her and I'm awfully fond of her and I hate myself for a beast if I ever hurt her little finger. We have a life together. And even if it can't last for ever, it is a life while it does last. And it might last as long as either of us lives. Who knows how long we've got to live? She is a delicate little thing, perhaps nobody but me knows how delicate. And as for me, I feel I might fall down the well any day. What I don't seem to see at all is you. When I think of what I've been and what I've done with you I'm afraid I am a few screws loose. I should be sorry to think that softening of the brain is setting in so soon, but that is what it seems like. You are such an absolute stranger and so different from what I'm used to and we don't seem to have a thing in common. As for love the word seems impossible. I know what love means even in Jill's case, and I know that in this affair with you it's an absolute impossibility. And then going to Canada. I'm sure I must have been clean off my chump when I promised such a thing. It makes me feel fairly frightened of myself. I feel I might do something really silly that I wasn't responsible for. And end my days in a lunatic asylum. You may think that's all I'm fit for after the way I've gone on, but it isn't a very nice thought for me. Thank goodness Jill is here and her being here makes me feel sane again, else I don't know what I might do, I might have an accident with the gun one evening. I love Jill and she makes me feel safe and sane, with her loving anger against me for being such a fool. Well what I want to say is won't you let us cry the whole thing off? I can't marry you, and really, I won't do such a thing if it seems to me wrong. It is all a great mistake. I've made a complete fool of myself, and all I can do is to apologize to you and ask you please to forget it and please to take no further notice of me. Your fox skin is nearly ready and seems all right. I will post it to you if you will let me know if this address is still right, and if you will accept my apology for the awful and lunatic way I have behaved with you, and then let the matter rest.

Jill sends her kindest regards. Her mother and father are staying with us over Christmas.

Yours very sincerely,

Ellen March.'

The boy read this letter in camp as he was cleaning his kit. He set his teeth and for a moment went almost pale, yellow round the eyes with fury. He said nothing and saw nothing and felt nothing but a livid rage that was quite unreasoning. Balked! Balked again!
5 Balked! He wanted the woman, he had fixed like doom upon having her. He felt that was his doom, his destiny, and his reward, to have this woman. She was his heaven and hell on earth, and he would have none elsewhere. Sightless with rage and thwarted madness he got through the morning. Save that in his mind he was
10 lurking and scheming towards an issue, he would have committed some insane act. Deep in himself he felt like roaring and howling and gnashing his teeth and breaking things. But he was too intelligent. He knew society was on top of him, and he must scheme. So with his teeth bitten together and his nose curiously slightly lifted,
15 like some creature that is vicious, and his eyes fixed and staring, he went through the morning's affairs drunk with anger and suppression. In his mind was one thing – Banford. He took no heed of all March's outpouring: none. One thorn rankled, stuck in his mind. Banford. In his mind, in his soul, in his whole being, one thorn
20 rankling to insanity. And he would have to get it out. He would have to get the thorn of Banford out of his life, if he died for it.

With this one fixed idea in his mind, he went to ask for twenty-four hours leave of absence. He knew it was not due to him. His consciousness was supernaturally keen. He knew where he must
25 go – he must go to the Captain. But how could he get at the Captain? In that great camp of wooden huts and tents he had no idea where his captain was.

But he went to the officers' canteen. There was his captain standing talking with three other officers. Henry stood in the door-
30 way at attention.

'May I speak to Captain Berryman?' The captain was Cornish like himself.

'What do you want?' called the captain.

'May I speak to you, Captain?'

35 'What do you want?' replied the captain, not stirring from among his group of fellow officers.

Henry watched his superior for a minute without speaking.

'You won't refuse me, sir, will you?' he asked gravely.

'It depends what it is.'

'Can I have twenty-four hours leave?'

'No, you've no business to ask.'

'I know I haven't. But I must ask you.'

'You've had your answer.'

'Don't sent me away, Captain.'

There was something strange about the boy as he stood there so everlasting in the doorway. The Cornish Captain felt the strangeness at once, and eyed him shrewdly.

'Why, what's afoot?' he said, curious.

'I'm in trouble about something. I must go to Blewbury,' said the boy.

'Blewbury, eh? After the girls?'

'Yes, it is a woman, Captain.' And the boy, as he stood there with his head reaching forward a little, went suddenly terribly pale, or yellow, and his lips seemed to give off pain. The captain saw and paled a little also. He turned aside.

'Go on then,' he said. 'But for God's sake don't cause any trouble of any sort.'

'I won't, Captain, thank you.'

He was gone. The captain, upset, took a gin and bitters. Henry managed to hire a bicycle. It was twelve o'clock when he left the camp. He had sixty miles of wet and muddy cross-roads to ride. But he was in the saddle and down the road without a thought of food.

At the farm, March was busy with a work she had had some time in hand. A bunch of Scotch-fir-trees stood at the end of the open shed, on a little bank where ran the fence between two of the gorse-shaggy meadows. The furthest of these trees was dead – it had died in the summer and stood with all its needles brown and sere in the air. It was not a very big tree. And it was absolutely dead. So March determined to have it, although they were not allowed to cut any of the timber. But it would make such splendid firing, in these days of scarce fuel.

She had been giving a few stealthy chops at the trunk for a week

or more, every now and then hacking away for five minutes, low down, near the ground, so no one should notice. She had not tried the saw, it was such hard work, alone. Now the tree stood with a great yawning gap in his base, perched as it were on one sinew,
5 and ready to fall. But he did not fall.

It was late in the damp December afternoon, with cold mists creeping out of the woods and up the hollows, and darkness waiting to sink in from above. There was a bit of yellowness where the sun was fading away beyond the low woods of the distance. March
10 took her axe and went to the tree. The small thud-thud of her blows resounded rather ineffectual about the wintry homestead. Banford came out wearing her thick coat, but with no hat on her head, so that her thin, bobbed hair blew on the uneasy wind that sounded in the pines and in the wood.

15 'What I'm afraid of,' said Banford, 'is that it will fall on the shed and we s'll have another job repairing that.'

'Oh, I don't think so,' said March, straightening herself and wiping her arm over her hot brow. She was flushed red, her eyes were very wide – open and queer, her upper lip lifted away from
20 her two white front teeth with a curious, almost rabbit-look.

A little stout man in a black overcoat and a bowler hat came pottering across the yard. He had a pink face and a white beard and smallish, pale-blue eyes. He was not very old, but nervy, and he walked with little short steps.

25 'What do you think, father?' said Banford. 'Don't you think it might hit the shed in falling?'

'Shed, no!' said the old man. 'Can't hit the shed. Might as well say the fence.'

'The fence doesn't matter,' said March, in her high voice.

30 'Wrong as usual, am I!' said Banford, wiping her straying hair from her eyes.

The tree stood as it were on one spelch of itself, leaning, and creaking in the wind. It grew on the bank of a little dry ditch between the two meadows. On the top of the bank straggled one
35 fence, running to the bushes uphill. Several trees clustered there in the corner of the field near the shed and near the gate which

led into the yard. Towards this gate, horizontal across the weary meadows came the grassy, rutted approach from the high road. There trailed another rickety fence, long split poles joining the short, thick, wide-apart uprights.

The three people stood at the back of the tree, in the corner of the shed meadow, just above the yard gate. The house with its two gables and its porch stood tidy in a little grassed garden across the yard. A little stout rosy-faced woman in a little red woollen shoulder shawl had come and taken her stand in the porch.

'Isn't it down yet?' she cried, in a high little voice.

'Just thinking about it,' called her husband. His tone towards the two girls was always rather mocking and satirical. March did not want to go on with her hitting while he was there. As for him, he wouldn't lift a stick from the ground if he could help it, complaining, like his daughter, of rheumatics in his shoulder. So the three stood there a moment silent in the cold afternoon, in the bottom corner near the yard.

They heard the far-off taps of a gate, and craned to look. Away across, on the green horizontal approach, a figure was just swinging on to a bicycle again, and lurching up and down over the grass, approaching.

'Why it's one of our boys – it's Jack,' said the old man.

'Can't be,' said Banford.

March craned her head to look. She alone recognized the khaki figure. She flushed, but said nothing.

'No, it isn't Jack, I don't think,' said the old man, staring with little round blue eyes under his white lashes.

In another moment the bicycle lurched into sight, and the rider dropped off at the gate. It was Henry, his face wet and red and spotted with mud. He was altogether a muddy sight.

'Oh!' cried Banford, as if afraid. 'Why, it's Henry!'

'What!' muttered the old man. He had a thick, rapid, muttering way of speaking, and was slightly deaf. 'What? What? Who is it? Who is it do you say? That young fellow? That young fellow of Nellie's? Oh! Oh!' And the satiric smile came on his pink face and white eyelashes.

Henry, pushing the wet hair off his steaming brow, had caught sight of them and heard what the old man said. His hot young face seemed to flame in the cold light.

'Oh, are you all there!' he said, giving his sudden, puppy's little
5 laugh. He was so hot and dazed with cycling he hardly knew where he was. He leaned the bicycle against the fence and climbed over into the corner on to the bank, without going in to the yard.

'Well, I must say, we weren't expecting you,' said Banford laconically.

10 'No, I suppose not,' said he, looking at March.

She stood aside, slack, with one knee drooped and the axe resting its head loosely on the ground. Her eyes were wide and vacant, and her upper lip lifted from her teeth in that helpless, fascinated rabbit-look. The moment she saw his glowing red face it was all
15 over with her. She was as helpless as if she had been bound. The moment she saw the way his head seemed to reach forward.

'Well, who is it? Who is it, anyway?' asked the smiling, satiric old man in his muttering voice.

'Why, Mr Grenfel, whom you've heard us tell about, father,'
20 said Banford coldly.

'Heard you tell about, I should think so. Heard of nothing else practically,' muttered the elderly man with his queer little jeering smile on his face. 'How do you do,' he added, suddenly reaching out his hand to Henry.

25 The boy shook hands just as startled. Then the two men fell apart.

'Cycled over from Salisbury Plain have you?' asked the old man.
'Yes.'

'Hm! Longish ride. How long d'it take you, eh? Some time, eh?
30 Several hours, I suppose.'

'About four.'

'Eh? Four! Yes, I should have thought so. When are you going back then?'

'I've got till tomorrow evening.'

35 'Till tomorrow evening, eh? Yes. Hm! Girls weren't expecting you, were they?'

And the old man turned his pale-blue, round little eyes under their white lashes mockingly towards the girls. Henry also looked round. He had become a little awkward. He looked at March, who was still staring away into the distance as if to see where the cattle were. Her hand was on the pommel of the axe, whose head rested loosely on the ground.

'What were you doing there?' he asked in his soft, courteous voice. 'Cutting a tree down?'

March seemed not to hear, as if in a trance.

'Yes,' said Banford. 'We've been at it for over a week.'

'Oh! And have you done it all by yourselves then?'

'Nellie's done it all, I've done nothing,' said Banford.

'Really! – You must have worked quite hard,' he said, addressing himself in a curious gentle tone direct to March. She did not answer, but remained half averted staring away towards the woods above as if in a trance.

'*Nellie!*' cried Banford sharply. 'Can't you answer?'

'What – me?' cried March starting round, and looking from one to the other. 'Did anyone speak to me?'

'Dreaming!' muttered the old man, turning aside to smile. 'Must be in love, eh, dreaming in the daytime!'

'Did you say anything to me?' said March, looking at the boy as from a strange distance, her eyes wide and doubtful, her face delicately flushed.

'I said you must have worked hard at the tree,' he replied courteously.

'Oh, that! Bit by bit. I thought it would have come down by now.'

'I'm thankful it hasn't come down in the night, to frighten us to death,' said Banford.

'Let me just finish it for you, shall I?' said the boy.

March slanted the axe-shaft in his direction.

'Would you like to?' she said.

'Yes, if you wish it,' he said.

'Oh, I'm thankful when the thing's down, that's all,' she replied, nonchalant.

'Which way is it going to fall?' said Banford. 'Will it hit the shed?'

'No, it won't hit the shed,' he said. 'I should think it will fall there – quite clear. Though it might give a twist and catch the fence.'

'Catch the fence!' cried the old man. 'What, catch the fence! When it's leaning at that angle? – Why it's farther off than the shed. It won't catch the fence.'

'No,' said Henry, 'I don't suppose it will. It has plenty of room to fall quite clear, and I suppose it will fall clear.'

'Won't tumble backwards on top of *us*, will it?' asked the old man, sarcastic.

'No, it won't do that,' said Henry, taking off his short overcoat and his tunic. 'Ducks! Ducks! Go back!'

A line of four brown-speckled ducks led by a brown-and-green drake were stemming away downhill from the upper meadow, coming like boats running on a ruffled sea, cockling their way top speed downwards towards the fence and towards the little group of people, and cackling as excitedly as if they brought the news of the Spanish Armada.

'Silly things! Silly things!' cried Banford going forward to turn them off. But they came eagerly towards her, opening their yellow-green beaks and quacking as if they were so excited to say something.

'There's no food. There's nothing here. You must wait a bit,' said Banford to them. 'Go away. Go away. Go round to the yard.'

They didn't go, so she climbed the fence to swerve them round under the gate and into the yard. So off they waggled in an excited string once more, wagging their rumps like the stems of little gondolas, ducking under the bar of the gate. Banford stood on the top of the bank, just over the fence, looking down on the other three.

Henry looked up at her, and met her queer, round-pupilled, weak eyes staring behind her spectacles. He was perfectly still. He looked away, up at the weak, leaning tree. And as he looked into the sky, like a huntsman who is watching a flying bird, he thought to himself: 'If the tree falls in just such a way, and spins just so much as it falls, then the branch there will strike her exactly as she stands on top of that bank.'

He looked at her again. She was wiping the hair from her brow again, with that perpetual gesture. In his heart he had decided her death. A terrible still force seemed in him, and a power that was just his. If he turned even a hair's breadth in the wrong direction, he would lose the power.

'Mind yourself, Miss Banford,' he said. And his heart held perfectly still, in the terrible pure will that she should not move.

'Who, me, mind myself?' she cried, her father's jeering tone in her voice. 'Why, do you think you might hit me with the axe?'

'No, it's just possible the tree might, though,' he answered soberly. But the tone of his voice seemed to her to imply that he was only being falsely solicitous and trying to make her move because it was his will to move her.

'Absolutely impossible,' she said.

He heard her. But he held himself icy still, lest he should lose his power.

'No, it's just possible. You'd better come down this way.'

'Oh, all right. Let us see some crack Canadian tree felling,' she retorted.

'Ready then,' he said, taking the axe, looking round to see he was clear.

There was a moment of pure, motionless suspense, when the world seemed to stand still. Then suddenly his form seemed to flash up enormously tall and fearful, he gave two swift, flashing blows, in immediate succession, the tree was severed, turning slowly, spinning strangely in the air and coming down like a sudden darkness on the earth. No one saw what was happening except himself. No one heard the strange little cry which Banford gave as the dark end of the bough swooped down, down on her. No one saw her crouch a little and receive the blow on the back of the neck. No one saw her flung outwards and laid, a little twitching heap, at the foot of the fence. No one except the boy. And he watched with intense bright eyes, as he would watch a wild goose he had shot. Was it winged, or dead? Dead!

Immediately he gave a loud cry. Immediately March gave a wild shriek that went far, far down the afternoon. And the father started a strange bellowing sound.

The boy leapt the fence and ran to the figure. The back of the neck and head was a mass of blood, of horror. He turned it over. The body was quivering with little convulsions. But she was dead really. He knew it, that it was so. He knew it in his soul and his
5 blood. The inner necessity of his life was fulfilling itself, it was he who was to live. The thorn was drawn out of his bowels. So, he put her down gently, she was dead.

He stood up. March was standing there petrified and absolutely motionless. Her face was dead white, her eyes big black pools. The
10 old man was scrambling horribly over the fence.

'I'm afraid it's killed her,' said the boy.

The old man was making curious, blubbering noises as he huddled over the fence.

'What!' cried March, starting electric.
15 'Yes, I'm afraid,' repeated the boy.

March was coming forward. The boy was over the fence before she reached it.

'What do you say, killed her?' she asked in a sharp voice.

'I'm afraid so,' he answered softly.
20 She went still whiter, fearful. The two stood facing one another. Her black eyes gazed on him with the last look of resistance. And then in a last agonized failure she began to grizzle, to cry in a shivery little fashion of a child that doesn't want to cry, but which is beaten from within, and gives that little first shudder of sobbing
25 which is not yet weeping, dry and fearful.

He had won. She stood there absolutely helpless, shuddering her dry sobs and her mouth trembling rapidly. And then, as in a child, with a little crash came the tears and the blind agony of sightless weeping. She sank down on the grass and sat there with
30 her hands on her breast and her face lifted in sightless, convulsed weeping. He stood above her, looking down on her, mute, pale, and everlasting seeming. He never moved, but looked down on her. And among all the torture of the scene, the torture of his own heart and bowels, he was glad, he had won.
35 After a long time he stooped to her and took her hands.

'Don't cry,' he said softly. 'Don't cry.'

She looked up at him with tears running from her eyes, a senseless look of helplessness and submission. So she gazed on him as if sightless, yet looking up to him. She would never leave him again. He had won her. And he knew it and was glad, because he wanted her for his life. His life must have her. And now he had won her. It was what his life must have.

But if he had won her, he had not yet got her. They were married at Christmas as he had planned, and he got again ten days leave. They went to Cornwall, to his own village, on the sea. He realized that it was awful for her to be at the farm any more.

But though she belonged to him, though she lived in his shadow, as if she could not be away from him, she was not happy. She did not want to leave him: and yet she did not feel free with him. Everything round her seemed to watch her, seemed to press on her. He had won her, he had her with him, she was his wife. And she – she belonged to him, she knew it. But she was not glad. And he was still foiled. He realized that though he was married to her and possessed her in every possible way, apparently, and though she *wanted* him to possess her, she wanted it, she wanted nothing else, now, still he did not quite succeed.

Something was missing. Instead of her soul swaying with new life, it seemed to droop, to bleed, as if it were wounded. She would sit for a long time with her hand in his, looking away at the sea. And in her dark, vacant eyes was a sort of wound, and her face looked a little peaked. If he spoke to her, she would turn to him with a faint new smile, the strange, quivering little smile of a woman who has died in the old way of love, and can't quite rise to the new way. She still felt she ought to *do* something, to strain herself in some direction. And there was nothing to do, and no direction in which to strain herself. And she could not quite accept the submergence which his new love put upon her. If she was in love, she ought to *exert* herself, in some way, loving. She felt the weary need of our day to *exert* herself in love. But she knew that in fact she must no more exert herself in love. He would not have the love which exerted itself towards him. It made his brow go black. No, he wouldn't let her exert her love towards him. No, she had to be

passive, to acquiesce, and to be submerged under the surface of love. She had to be like the seaweeds she saw as she peered down from the boat, swaying forever delicately under water, with all their delicate fibrils put tenderly out upon the flood, sensitive, utterly
5 sensitive and receptive within the shadowy sea, and never, never rising and looking forth above water while they lived. Never. Never looking forth from the water until they died, only then washing, corpses, upon the surface. But while they lived, always submerged, always beneath the wave. Beneath the wave they might have power-
10 ful roots, stronger than iron, they might be tenacious and dangerous in their soft waving within the flood. Beneath the water they might be stronger, more indestructible than resistant oak trees are on land. But it was always under-water, always under-water. And she, being a woman, must be like that.

15   And she had been so used to the very opposite. She had had to take all the thought for love and for life, and all the responsibility. Day after day she had been responsible for the coming day, for the coming year: for her dear Jill's health and happiness and well-being. Verily, in her own small way, she had felt herself responsible for
20 the well-being of the world. And this had been her great stimulant, this grand feeling that, in her own small sphere, she was responsible for the well-being of the world.

And she had failed. She knew that, even in her small way, she had failed. She had failed to satisfy her own feeling of responsibility.
25 It was so difficult. It seemed so grand and easy at first. And the more you tried, the more difficult it became. It had seemed so easy to make one beloved creature happy. And the more you tried, the worse the failure. It was terrible. She had been all her life reaching, reaching, and what she reached for seemed so near, until she had
30 stretched to her utmost limit. And then it was always beyond her.

Always beyond her, vaguely, unrealizably beyond her, and she was left with nothingness at last. The life she reached for, the happiness she reached for, the well-being she reached for all slipped back, became unreal, the further she stretched her hand. She
35 wanted some goal, some finality – and there was none. Always this ghastly reaching, reaching, striving for something that might be

just beyond. Even to make Jill happy. She was glad Jill was dead. For she had realized that she could never make her happy. Jill would always be fretting herself thinner and thinner, weaker and weaker. Her pains grew worse instead of less. It would be so for ever. She was glad she was dead. 5

And if she had married a man it would have been just the same. The woman striving, striving to make the man happy, striving within her own limits for the well-being of her world. And always achieving failure. Little, foolish successes in money or in ambition. But at the very point where she most wanted success, in the 10 anguished effort to make some one beloved human being happy and perfect, there the failure was almost catastrophic. You wanted to make your beloved happy, and his happiness seemed always achievable. If only you did just this, that and the other. And you did this, that, and the other, in all good faith, and every time the 15 failure became a little more ghastly. You could love yourself to ribbons, and strive and strain yourself to the bone, and things would go from bad to worse, bad to worse, as far as happiness went. The awful mistake of happiness.

Poor March, in her goodwill and her responsibility, she had 20 strained herself till it seemed to her that the whole of life and everything was only a horrible abyss of nothingness. The more you reached after the fatal flower of happiness, which trembles so blue and lovely in a crevice just beyond your grasp, the more fearfully you became aware of the ghastly and awful gulf of the precipice 25 below you, into which you will inevitably plunge, as into the bottomless pit, if you reach any further. You pluck flower after flower – it is never *the* flower. The flower itself – its calyx is a horrible gulf, it is the bottomless pit.

That is the whole history of the search for happiness, whether it 30 be your own or somebody else's that you want to win. It ends, and it always ends, in the ghastly sense of the bottomless nothingness into which you will inevitably fall if you strain any further.

And women? – what goal can any woman conceive, except happiness? Just happiness, for herself and the whole world. That, 35 and nothing else. And so, she assumes the responsibility and sets off towards her goal. She can see it there, at the foot of the rainbow. Or she can see it a little way beyond, in the blue distance. Not far, not far.

But the end of the rainbow is a bottomless gulf down which you
5 can fall forever without arriving, and the blue distance is a void pit which can swallow you and all your efforts into its emptiness, and still be no emptier. You and all your efforts. So, the illusion of attainable happiness!

Poor March, she had set off so wonderfully, towards the blue
10 goal. And the further and further she had gone, the more fearful had become the realization of emptiness. An agony, an insanity at last.

She was glad it was over. She was glad to sit on the shore and look westwards over the sea, and know the great strain had ended.
15 She would never strain for love and happiness any more. And Jill was safely dead. Poor Jill, poor Jill. It must be sweet to be dead.

For her own part, death was not her destiny. She would have to leave her destiny to the boy. But then, the boy. He wanted more than that. He wanted her to give herself without defences, to sink
20 and become submerged in him. And she – she wanted to sit still, like a woman on the last milestone, and watch. She wanted to see, to know, to understand. She wanted to be alone: with him at her side.

And he! He did not want her to watch any more, to see any
25 more, to understand any more. He wanted to veil her woman's spirit, as Orientals veil the woman's face. He wanted her to commit herself to him, and to put her independent spirit to sleep. He wanted to take away from her all her effort, all that seemed her very *raison d'être*. He wanted to make her submit, yield, blindly
30 pass away out of all her strenuous consciousness. He wanted to take away her consciousness, and make her just his woman. Just his woman.

And she was so tired, so tired, like a child that wants to go to sleep, but which fights against sleep as if sleep were death. She
35 seemed to stretch her eyes wider in the obstinate effort and tension of keeping awake. She *would* keep awake. She *would* know. She

would consider and judge and decide. She *would* have the reins of her own life between her own hands. She *would* be an independent woman to the last. But she was so tired, so tired of everything. And sleep seemed near. And there was such rest in the boy.

Yet there, sitting in a niche of the high wild cliffs of West Cornwall, looking over the westward sea, she stretched her eyes wider and wider. Away to the West, Canada, America. She *would* know and she *would* see what was ahead. And the boy, sitting beside her staring down at the gulls, had a cloud between his brows and the strain of discontent in his eyes. He wanted her asleep, at peace in him. He wanted her at peace, asleep in him. And *there* she was, dying with the strain of her own wakefulness. Yet she would not sleep: no, never. Sometimes he thought bitterly that he ought to have left her. He ought never to have killed Banford. He should have left Banford and March to kill one another.

But that was only impatience: and he knew it. He was waiting, waiting to go west. He was aching almost in torment to leave England, to go west, to take March away. To leave this shore! He believed that as they crossed the seas, as they left this England which he so hated, because in some way it seemed to have stung him with poison, she would go to sleep. She would close her eyes at last, and give in to him.

And then he would have her, and he would have his own life at last. He chafed, feeling he hadn't got his own life. He would never have it till she yielded and slept in him. Then he would have all his own life as a young man and a male, and she would have all her own life as a woman and a female. There would be no more of this awful straining. She would not be a man any more, an independent woman with a man's responsibility. Nay, even the responsibility for her own soul she would have to commit to him. He knew it was so, and obstinately held out against her, waiting for the surrender.

'You'll feel better when once we get over the seas, to Canada, over there,' he said to her as they sat among the rocks on the cliff.

She looked away to the sea's horizon, as if it were not real. Then she looked round at him, with the strained, strange look of a child that is struggling against sleep.

'Shall I?' she said.

'Yes,' he answered quietly.

And her eyelids dropped with the slow motion, sleep weighing them unconscious. But she pulled them open again to say:

5   'Yes, I may. I can't tell. I can't tell what it will be like over there.'

'If only we could go soon!' he said, with pain in his voice.

The Flying Fish

1 Departure from Mexico

'Come home else no Day in Daybrook.' This cablegram was the first thing Gethin Day read of the pile of mail which he found at the hotel in the lost town of South Mexico, when he returned from his trip to the coast. Though the message was not signed, he knew whom it came from and what it meant. 5

He lay in his bed in the hot October evening, still sick with malaria. In the flush of fever he saw yet the parched, stark mountains of the south, the villages of reed huts lurking among trees, the black-eyed natives with the lethargy, the ennui, the pathos, the beauty of an exhausted race; and above all he saw 10 the weird, uncanny flowers, which he had hunted from the high plateaux, through the valleys, and down to the steaming crocodile heat of the *tierra caliente*, towards the sandy, burning, intolerable shores. For he was fascinated by the mysterious green blood that runs in the veins of plants, and the purple and yellow and red blood 15 that colours the faces of flowers. Especially the unknown flora of South Mexico attracted him, and above all he wanted to trace to the living plant the mysterious essences and toxins known with such strange elaboration to the Mayas, the Zapotecas, and the Aztecs. 20

His head was humming like a mosquito, his legs were paralysed for the moment by the heavy quinine injection the doctor had injected into them, and his soul was as good as dead with the malaria; so he threw all his letters unopened on the floor, hoping never to see them again. He lay with the pale yellow cablegram in 25

his hand: 'Come home else no Day in Daybrook.' Through the
open doors from the patio of the hotel came the heavy scent of that
invisible green night-flower the natives call *Buena de Noche*. The
little Mexican servant-girl strode in barefoot with a cup of tea, her
5 flounced cotton skirt swinging, her long black hair down her back.
She asked him in her birdlike Spanish if he wanted nothing more.
'*Nada más*,' he said. 'Nothing more; leave me and shut the door.'

He wanted to shut out the scent of that powerful green
inconspicuous night-flower he knew so well.

10   No Day in Daybrook;
                       For the Vale a bad outlook.

No Day in Daybrook! There had been Days in Daybrook since
time began: at least, so he imagined.

Daybrook was a sixteenth-century stone house, among the hills
15 in the middle of England. It stood where Crichdale bends to the
south and where Ashleydale joins in. 'Daybrook standeth at the
junction of the ways and at the centre of the trefoil. Even it rides
within the Vale as an ark between three seas; being indeed the ark
of these vales, if not of all England.' So had written Sir Gilbert
20 Day, he who built the present Daybrook in the sixteenth century.
Sir Gilbert's *Book of Days*, so beautifully written out on vellum
and illuminated by his own hand, was one of the treasures of the
family.

Sir Gilbert had sailed the Spanish seas in his day, and had come
25 home rich enough to rebuild the old house of Daybrook according
to his own fancy. He had made it a beautiful pointed house, rather
small, standing upon a knoll above the river Ashe, where the valley
narrowed and the woods rose steep behind. 'Nay,' wrote this quaint
Elizabethan, 'though I say that Daybrook is the ark of the Vale, I
30 mean not the house itself, but He that Day, that lives in the house
in his day. While Day there be in Daybrook, the floods shall not
cover the Vale nor shall they ride over England completely.'

Gethin Day was nearing forty, and he had not spent much of his
time in Daybrook. He had been a soldier and had wandered in
35 many countries. At home his sister Lydia, twenty years older than

himself, had been the Day in Daybrook. Now from her cablegram he knew she was either ill or already dead.

She had been rather hard and grey like the rock of Crichdale, but faithful and a pillar of strength. She had let him go his own way, but always when he came home, she would look into his blue eyes with her searching uncanny grey look and ask: 'Well, have you come, or are you still wandering?' 'Still wandering, I think,' he said. 'Mind you don't wander into a cage one of these days,' she replied; 'you would find far more room for yourself in Daybrook than in these foreign parts, if you knew how to come into your own.'

This had always been the burden of her song to him: *if you knew how to come into your own.* And it had always exasperated him with a sense of futility; though whether his own futility or Lydia's, he had never made out.

Lydia was wrapt up in old Sir Gilbert's *Book of Days*; she had written out for her brother a fair copy, neatly bound in green leather, and had given it him without a word when he came of age, merely looking at him with that uncanny look of her grey eyes, expecting something of him, which always made him start away from her.

The *Book of Days* was a sort of secret family bible at Daybrook. It was never shown to strangers, nor ever mentioned outside the immediate family. Indeed in the family it was never openly alluded to. Only on solemn occasions, or on rare evenings, at twilight, when the evening star shone, had the father, now dead, occasionally read aloud to the two children from the nameless work.

In the copy she had written out for Gethin, Lydia had used different coloured inks in different places. Gethin imagined that her favourite passages were those in the royal-blue ink, where the page was almost as blue as the cornflowers that grew tall beside the walks in the garden at Daybrook.

'Beauteous is the day of the yellow sun which is the common day of men; but even as the winds roll unceasing above the trees of the world, so doth that Greater Day, which is the Uncommon Day, roll over the unclipt bushes of our little daytime. Even also as the

morning sun shakes his yellow wings on the horizon and rises up,
so the great bird beyond him spreads out his dark blue feathers,
and beats his wings in the tremor of the Greater Day.'

Gethin knew a great deal of his *Book of Days* by heart. In a
5 dilettante fashion, he had always liked rather highflown poetry, but
in the last years, something in the hard, fierce, finite sun of Mexico,
in the dry terrible land, and in the black staring eyes of the
suspicious natives, had made the ordinary day lose its reality to
him. It had cracked like some great bubble, and to his uneasiness
10 and terror, he had seemed to see through the fissures the deeper
blue of that other Greater Day where moved the other sun shaking
its dark blue wings. Perhaps it was the malaria; perhaps it was his
own inevitable development; perhaps it was the presence of those
handsome, dangerous, wide-eyed men left over from the ages
15 before the flood in Mexico, which caused his old connections
and his accustomed world to break for him. He was ill, and he felt
as if at the very middle of him, beneath his navel, some membrane
were torn, some membrane which had connected him with the
world and its day. The natives who attended him, quiet, soft,
20 heavy, and rather helpless, seemed, he realized, to be gazing from
their wide black eyes always into that greater day whence they had
come and where they wished to return. Men of a dying race, to
whom the busy sphere of the common day is a cracked and leaking
shell.

25 He wanted to go home. He didn't care now whether England
was tight and little and over-crowded and far too full of furniture.
He no longer minded the curious quiet atmosphere of Daybrook
in which he had felt he would stifle as a young man. He no longer
resented the weight of family tradition, nor the peculiar sense of
30 authority which the house seemed to have over him. Now he was
sick from the soul outwards, and the common day had cracked for
him, and the uncommon day was showing him its immensity, he
felt that home was the place. It did not matter that England was
small and tight and over-furnished, if the Greater Day were round
35 about. He wanted to go home, away from these big wild countries
where men were dying back into the Greater Day, home where he

dare face the sun behind the sun, and come into his own in the Greater Day.

But he was as yet too ill to go. He lay in the nausea of the tropics, and let the days pass over him. The door of his room stood open on to the patio where green banana trees and high strange-sapped flowering shrubs rose from the water-sprinkled earth towards that strange rage of blue which was the sky over the shadow-heavy, perfume-soggy air of the closed-in courtyard. Dark-blue shadows moved from the side of the patio, disappeared, then appeared on the other side. Evening had come, and the barefoot natives in white calico flitted with silent rapidity across, and across, for ever going, yet mysteriously going nowhere, threading the timelessness with their transit, like swallows of darkness.

The window of the room, opposite the door, opened on to the tropical parched street. It was a big window, came nearly down to the floor, and was heavily barred with upright and horizontal bars. Past the window went the natives, with the soft, light rustle of their sandals. Big straw hats balanced, dark cheeks, calico shoulders brushed with the silent swiftness of the Indian past the barred window-space. Sometimes children clutched the bars and gazed in, with great shining eyes and straight blue-black hair, to see the Americano lying in the majesty of a white bed. Sometimes a beggar stood there, sticking a skinny hand through the iron grille and whimpering the strange, endless, pullulating whimper of the beggar – '*por amor de Dios!*' – on and on and on, as it seemed for an eternity. But the sick man on the bed endured it with the same endless endurance in resistance, endurance in resistance which he had learned in the Indian countries. Aztec or Mixtec, Zapotec or Maya, always the same power of serpent-like torpor of resistance.

The doctor came – an educated Indian: though he could do nothing but inject quinine and give a dose of calomel. But he was lost between the two days, the fatal greater day of the Indians, the fussy, busy lesser day of the white people.

'How is it going to finish?' he said to the sick man, seeking a word. 'How is it going to finish with the Indians, with the Mexicans? Now the soldiers are all taking *marihuana* – hashish!'

'They are all going to die. They are all going to kill themselves –
all – all,' said the Englishman, in the faint permanent delirium of
his malaria. 'After all, beautiful it is to be dead, and quite departed.'

The doctor looked at him in silence, understanding only too
5 well. 'Beautiful it is to be dead!' It is the refrain which hums at the
centre of every Indian heart, where the greater day is hemmed in
by the lesser. The despair that comes when the lesser day hems in
the greater. Yet the doctor looked at the gaunt white man in malice:
– 'What, would you have us quite gone, you Americans?'

10 At last, Gethin Day crawled out into the plaza. The square was
like a great low fountain of green and of dark shade, now it was
autumn and the rains were over. Scarlet craters rose the canna
flowers, licking great red tongues, and tropical yellow. Scarlet,
yellow, green, blue-green, sunshine intense and invisible, deep
15 indigo shade! and small, white-clad natives pass, passing, across
the square, through the green lawns, under the indigo shade, and
across the hollow sunshine of the road into the arched arcades of
the low Spanish buildings, where the shops were. The low, baroque
Spanish buildings stood back with a heavy, sick look, as if they too
20 felt the endless malaria in their bowels, the greater day of the stony
Indian crushing the more jaunty, lean European day which they
represented. The yellow cathedral leaned its squat, earthquake-
shaken towers, the bells sounded hollow. Earth-coloured tiny
soldiers lay and stood around the entrance to the municipal palace,
25 which was so baroque and Spanish, but which now belonged to
the natives. Heavy as a strange bell of shadow-coloured glass, the
shadow of the greater day hung over this coloured plaza which the
Europeans had created, like an oasis, in the lost depths of Mexico.
Gethin Day sat half lying on one of the broken benches, while
30 tropical birds flew and twittered in the great trees, and natives
twittered or flitted in silence, and he knew that here, the European
day was annulled again. His body was sick with the poison that
lurks in all tropical air, his soul was sick with that other day, that
rather awful greater day which permeates the little days of the old
35 races. He wanted to get out, to get out of this ghastly tropical void
into which he had fallen.

Yet it was the end of November before he could go. Little revolutions had again broken the thread of railway at the end of which the southern town hung revolving like a spider. It was a narrow-gauge railway, one single narrow little track which ran over the plateau, then slipped down, down the long *barranca*, 5 descending five thousand feet down to the valley which was a cleft in the plateau, then up again seven thousand feet, to the higher plateau to the north. How easy to break the thread! One of the innumerable little wooden bridges destroyed, and it was done. The three hundred miles to the north were impassable wilderness, like 10 the hundred and fifty miles through the low-lying jungle to the south.

At last however he could crawl away. The train came again. He had cabled to England, and had received the answer that his sister was dead. It seemed so natural, there under the powerful November 15 sun of southern Mexico, in the drugging powerful odours of the night-flowers, that Lydia should be dead. She seemed so much more *real*, shall we say actually vital, in death. Dead, he could think of her as quite near and comforting and real, whereas while she was alive, she was so utterly alien, remote and fussy, ghost-like in 20 her petty Derbyshire day.

'For the little day is like a house with the family round the hearth, and the door shut. Yet outside whispers the Greater Day, wall-less, and hearthless. And the time will come at last when the walls of the little day shall fall, and what is left of the family of men shall 25 find themselves outdoors in the Greater Day, houseless and abroad, even here between the knees of the Vales, even in Crichdale. It is a doom that will come upon tall men. And then they will breathe deep, and be breathless in the great air, and salt sweat will stand on their brow, thick as buds on sloe-bushes when the sun comes 30 back. And little men will shudder and die out, like clouds of grasshoppers falling in the sea. Then tall men will remain alone in the land, moving deeper in the Greater Day, and moving deeper. Even as the flying fish, when he leaves the air and recovereth his element in the depth, plunges and invisibly rejoices. So will tall 35 men rejoice, after their flight of fear, through the thin air, pursued

by death. For it is on wings of fear, sped from the mouth of death, that the flying fish riseth twinkling in the air, and rustles in astonishment silvery through the thin small day. But he dives again into the great peace of the deeper day, and under the belly of death,
5 and passes into his own.'

Gethin read again his *Book of Days*, in the twilight of his last evening. Personally, he resented the symbolism and mysticism of his Elizabethan ancestor. But it was in his veins. And he was going home, back, back to the house with the flying fish on the roof. He
10 felt an immense doom over everything, still the same next morning, when, an hour after dawn, the little train ran out from the doomed little town, on to the plateau, where the cactus thrust up its fluted tubes, and where the mountains stood back, blue, cornflower-blue, so dark and pure in form, in the land of the Greater Day, the day
15 of demons. The little train, with two coaches, one full of natives, the other with four or five 'white' Mexicans, ran fussily on, in the little day of toys and men's machines. On the roof sat tiny, earthy-looking soldiers, faces burnt black, with cartridge-belts and rifles. They clung on tight, not to be shaken off. And away went
20 this weird toy, this crazy little caravan, over the great lost land of cacti and mountains standing back, on to the shut-in defile where the long descent began.

At half-past ten, at a station some distance down the *barranca*, a station connected with old silver mines, the train stood, and all
25 descended to eat: the eternal turkey with black sauce, potatoes, salad, and apple pie – the American apple pie, which is a sandwich of cooked apple between two layers of pie-crust. And also beer, from Puebla. Two Chinamen administered the dinner, in all the decency, cleanness and well-cookedness of the little day of the
30 white men, which they reproduce so well. There it was, the little day of our civilization. Outside, the little train waited. The little black-faced soldiers sharpened their knives. The vast, varying declivity of the *barranca* stood in sun and shadow as on the day of doom, untouched.

35 On again, winding, descending the huge and savage gully or crack in the plateau-edge, where no men lived. Bushes trailed with

elegant pink creeper, such as is seen in hothouses, enormous blue convolvuluses opened out, and in the unseemly tangle of growth, bulbous orchids jutted out from trees, and let hang a trail of white or yellow flower. The strange, entangled squalor of the jungle.

Gethin Day looked down the ravine, where water was running. He saw four small deer lifting their heads from drinking, to look at the train. '*Los venados! los venados!*' he heard the soldiers softly calling. As if knowing they were safe, the deer stood and wondered, away there in the Greater Day, in the manless space, while the train curled round a sharp jutting rock.

They came at last to the bottom, where it was very hot, and a few wild men hung round with the sword-like knives of the sugar-cane. The train seemed to tremble with fear all the time, as if its thread might be cut. So frail, so thin the thread of the lesser day, threading with its business the great reckless heat of the savage land. So frail a thread, so easily snapped!

But the train crept on, northwards, upwards. And as the stupor of heat began to pass, in the later afternoon, the sick man saw among mango trees, beyond the bright green stretches of sugar-cane, white clusters of a village, with the coloured dome of a church all yellow and blue with shiny majolica tiles. Spain putting the bubbles of her little day among the blackish trees of the unconquerable.

He came at nightfall to a small square town, more in touch with civilization, where the train ended its frightened run. He slept there. And next day he took another scrap of a train across to the edge of the main plateau. The country was wild, but more populous. An occasional big *hacienda* with sugar-mills stood back among the hills. But it was silent. Spain had spent the energy of her little day here, now the silence, the terror of the Greater Day, mysterious with death, was filling in again.

On the train a native, a big, handsome man, wandered back and forth among the uneasy Mexican travellers with a tray of glasses of ice-cream. He was no doubt of the Tlascala tribe. Gethin Day looked at him and met his glistening dark eyes. '*Quiere helados, Señor?*' said the Indian, reaching a glass with his dark, subtle-skinned, workless hand. And in the soft, secret tones of his voice, Gethin Day heard the sound of the Greater Day. *'Gracias!'*

'Padrón! Padrón!' moaned a woman at the station. *'Por amor de Dios, Padrón!'* and she held out her hand for a few centavos. And in the moaning croon of her Indian voice the Englishman heard again the fathomless crooning appeal of the Indian women, moaning stranger, more terrible than the ring-dove, with a sadness that had no horizon, and a rocking, moaning appeal that drew out the very marrow of the soul of a man. Over the door of her womb was written not only: *'Lasciate ogni speranza, voi ch'entrate,'* but: *'Perdite ogni pianto, voi ch'uscite.'* For the men who had known these women were beyond weeping and beyond even despair, mute in the timeless compulsion of the Greater Day. Big, proud men could sell glasses of ice-cream at twenty-five centavos, and not really know they were doing it. They were elsewhere, beyond despair. Only sometimes the last passion of the death-lust would sweep them, shut up as they were in the white man's lesser day, belonging as they did to the greater day.

The little train ran on to the main plateau, and to the junction with the main-line railway called the Queen's Own, a railway that still belongs to the English, and that joins Mexico City with the Gulf of Mexico. Here, in the big but forlorn railway restaurant the Englishman ordered the regular meal, that came with American mechanical take-it-or-leave-it flatness. He ate what he could, and went out again. There the vast plains were level and bare, under the blue winter sky, so pure, and not too hot, and in the distance the white cone of the volcano of Orizaba stood perfect in the middle air.

'There is no help. O man. Fear gives thee wings like a bird, death comes after thee open-mouthed, and thou soarest on the wind like a fly. But thy flight is not far, and thy flying is not long. Thou art a fish of the timeless Ocean, and must needs fall back. Take heed lest thou break thyself in the fall! For death is not in dying, but in the fear. Cease then the struggle of thy flight, and fall back into the deep element where death is and is not, and life is not a fleeing away. It is a beauteous thing to live and to be alive. Live then in the Greater Day, and let the waters carry thee, and the flood bear thee along, and live, only live, no more of this hurrying away.'

'No more of this hurrying away.' Even the Elizabethans had known it, the restlessness, the 'hurrying away'. Gethin Day knew he had been hurrying away. He had hurried perhaps a little too far, just over the edge. Now, try as he might, he was aware of a gap in his time-space *continuum*; he was, in the words of his ancestor, aware of the Greater Day showing through the cracks in the ordinary day. And it was useless trying to fill up the cracks. The little day was destined to crumble away, as far as he was concerned, and he would *have* to inhabit the greater day. The very sight of the volcano cone in mid-air made him know it. His little self was used up, worn out. He felt sick and frail, facing this change of life.

'Be still, then, be still! Wrap thyself in patience, shroud thyself in peace, as the tall volcano clothes himself in snow. Yet he looks down in him, and sees wet sun in him molten and of great force, stirring with the scald sperm of life. Be still, above the sperm of life, which spills alone in its hour. Be still, as an apple on its core, as a nightingale in winter, as a long-waiting mountain upon its fire. Be still, upon thine own sun.

'For thou hast a sun in thee. Thou hast a sun in thee, and it is not timed. Therefore wait. Wait, and be at peace with thine own sun, which is thy sperm of life. Be at peace with thy sun in thee, as the volcano is, and the dark holly-bush before berry-time, and the long hours of night. Abide by thy sun in thee, even the onion doth so, though you see it not. Yet peel her, and her sun in thine eyes maketh tears. Each thing hath its little sun, even in the wicked house-fly something twinkleth.'

Standing there on the platform of the station open to the great plains of the plateau, Gethin Day said to himself: My old ancestor is more real to me than the restaurant, and the dinner I have eaten, after all. The train still did not come. He turned to another page of cornflower-blue writing, hoping to find something amusing.

'When earth inert lieth too heavy, then Vesuvius spitteth out fire. And if a nightingale would not sing, his song unsung in him would slay him. For to the nightingale his song is Nemesis, and unsung songs are the Erinyes, the impure Furies of vengeance. And thy sun in thee is thy all in all, so be patient, and take no care. Take no care, for what thou knowest is ever less than what thou art. The full fire even of thine own sun in thine own body, thou canst never know. So how shouldst thou load care upon thy sun? Take heed, take thought, take pleasure, take pain, take all things as thy sun stirs. Only fasten not thyself in care about anything, for care is impiety, it spits upon the sun.'

It was the white and still volcano, visionary across the swept plain, that looked back at him as he glanced up from his *Book of Days*. But there the train came, thundering, with all the mock majesty of great equipage, and the Englishman entered the Pullman car, and sat with his book in his pocket.

The train, almost with the splendour of the Greater Day, yet rickety and foolish at last, raced on the level, entered the defile, and crept, cautiously twining round and round, down the cliff-face of the plateau, with the low lands lying thousands of feet below, specked with a village or two like fine specks. Yet the low lands drew up, and the pine trees were gone far above, and at last the thick trees crowded the line, and dark-faced natives ran beside the train selling gardenias, gardenia perfume heavy in all the air. But the train was nearly empty.

Veracruz at night-fall was a modern stone port, but disheartened and tropical, mostly shut up, abandoned, as if life had quietly left it. Great customs buildings, unworking, acres of pianofortes in packing-cases, all the endless jetsam of the little day of commerce flung up here and waiting, acres of goods unattended to, waiting till the labour of Veracruz should cease to be on strike. A town, a port struck numb, the inner sun striking vengefully at the little life of commerce. The day's sun set, there was a heavy orange light over the waters, something sinister, a gloom, a deep resentment in nature, even in the washing of the warm sea. In these salt waters natives were still baptized to Christianity, and the socialists, in mockery perhaps, baptized themselves into the mystery of frustration and revenge. The port was in the hands of strikers and wild out-of-workers, and was blank. Officials had almost disappeared. Even here, a woman, a 'lady' examined the passports.

But the ship rode at the end of the jetty: the one lonely passenger ship. There was one other steamer – from Sweden, a cargo boat. For the rest, the port was deserted. It was a point where the wild primeval day of this continent met the busy white man's day, and the two annulled one another. The result was a port of nullity, nihilism concrete and actual, calling itself the city of the True Cross.

2 The Gulf

In the morning they sailed off, away from the hot shores, from the high land hanging up inwards. And world gives place to world. In an hour, it was only ship and ocean, the world of land and affairs was gone.

There were few people on board. In the second-class saloon only seventeen souls. Gethin Day was travelling second. It was a German boat, he knew it would be clean and comfortable. The second-class fare was already forty-five pounds. And a man who is not rich, and who would live his life under as little compulsion as possible, must calculate keenly with money and its power. For the lesser day of money and the mealy-mouthed Mammon is always ready for a victim, and a man who has glimpsed the Greater Day, and the inward sun, will not fall into the clutches of Mammon's mean day, if he can help it. Gethin Day had a moderate income, and he looked on this as his bulwark against Mammon's despicable authority. The thought of earning a living was repulsive and humiliating to him.

In the first-class saloon were only four persons: two Danish merchants, stout and wealthy, who had been part of a bunch of Danish business men invited by the Mexican government to look at the business resources of the land. They had been fêted and feasted, and shown what they were meant to see, so now, fuller of business than ever, they were going back to Copenhagen to hatch the eggs they had conceived. But they had also eaten oysters in Veracruz, and the oysters also were inside them. They fell sick of poison, and lay deathly ill all the voyage, leaving the only other first-class passengers, an English knight and his son, alone in their glory. Gethin Day was sincerely glad he had escaped the first class, for the voyage was twenty days.

5 The seventeen souls of the second class were four of them English, two Danish, five Spaniards, five Germans, and a Cuban. They all sat at one long table in the dining-saloon, the Cuban at one end of the table, flanked by four English on his left, facing the five Spaniards across the table. Then came the two Danes, facing
10 one another, and being buffer-state between the rest and the five Germans, who occupied the far end of the table. It was a German boat, so the Germans were very noisy, and the stewards served them first. The Spaniards and the Cuban were mum, the English were stiff, the Danes were uneasy, the Germans were boisterous,
15 and so the first luncheon passed. It was the lesser day of the ship, and small enough. The menu being in correct German and doubtful Spanish, the Englishwoman on Gethin Day's right put up a lorgnette and stared at it. She was unable to stare it out of countenance, so she put it down and ate uninformed as to what
20 she was eating. The Spaniard opposite Gethin Day had come to table without collar or tie, doing the bluff, go-to-hell colonial touch, almost in his shirt-sleeves. He was a man of about thirty-two. He brayed at the steward in strange, harsh Galician Spanish, the steward grinned somewhat sneeringly and answered in German,
25 having failed to understand, and not prepared to exert himself to try. Down the table a blonde horse of a woman was shouting at the top of her voice, in harsh North-German, to a Herr Doktor with turned-up moustaches who presided at the German head of the table. The Spaniards bent forward in a row to look with a sort of
30 silent horror at the yelling woman, then they looked at one another with a faint grimace of mocking repulsion. The Galician banged the table with the empty wine-decanter: wine was 'included'. The steward, with a sneering little grin at such table-manners, brought a decanter half full. Wine was not *ad lib.*, but *à discrétion*. The
35 Spaniards, having realized this, henceforth snatched it quickly and pretty well emptied the decanter before the English got a shot at

it. Which somewhat amused the table-stewards, who wanted to see the two foreign lots fight it out. But Gethin Day solved this problem by holding out his hand to the fat, clean-shaven Basque, as soon as the decanter reached that gentleman, and saying: 'May I serve the lady?' Whereupon the Basque handed over the decanter, and Gethin helped the two ladies and himself, before handing back the decanter to the Spaniards. – Man wants but little here below, but he's damn well got to see he gets it. – All this is part of the little day, which has to be seen to. Whether it is interesting or not depends on one's state of soul.

Bristling with all the bristles of offence and defence which a man has to put up the first days in such a company, Gethin Day would go off down the narrow gangway of the bottom deck, down into the steerage, where the few passengers lay about in shirt and trousers, on to the very front tip of the boat.

She was a long, narrow, old ship, long like a cigar, and not much space in her. Yet she was pleasant, and had a certain grace of her own, was a real ship, not merely a 'liner'. She seemed to travel swift and clean, piercing away into the Gulf.

Gethin Day would sit for hours at the very tip of the ship, on the bowsprit, looking out into the whitish sunshine of the hot Gulf of Mexico. Here he was alone, and the world was all strange white sunshine, candid, and water, warm, bright water, perfectly pure beneath him, of an exquisite frail green. It lifted vivid wings from the running tip of the ship, and threw white pinion-spray from its green edges. And always, always, always it was in the two-winged fountain, as the ship came like life between, and always the spray fell swishing, pattering from the green arch of the water-wings. And below, as yet untouched, a moment ahead, always a moment ahead, and perfectly untouched, was the lovely green depth of the water, depth, deep, shallow-pale emerald above an under sapphire-green, dark and pale, blue and shimmer-green, two waters, many waters, one water, perfect in unison, one moment ahead of the ship's bows, so serene, fathomless and pure and free of time. It was very lovely, and on the softly-lifting bowsprit of the long, swift ship the body was cradled in the sway of timeless life, the soul lay in the jewel-coloured moment, the jewel-pure eternity of this gulf of nowhere.

And always, always, like a dream, the flocks of flying fish swept into the air, from nowhere, and went brilliantly twinkling in their
5 flight of silvery watery wings rapidly fluttering, away, low as swallows over the smooth curved surface of the sea, then gone again, vanished, without splash or evidence, gone. One alone like a little silver twinkle. Gone! The sea was still and silky-surfaced, blue and softly heaving, empty, purity itself, sea, sea, sea.

10 Then suddenly the faint whispering crackle, and a cloud of silver on webs of pure, fluttering water was soaring low over the surface of the sea, at an angle from the ship, as if jetted away from the cut-water soaring in a low arc, fluttering with the wild emphasis of grasshoppers or locusts suddenly burst out of the grass, in a wild
15 rush to make away, make away, and making it, away, away, then suddenly gone, like a lot of lights blown out in one breath. And still the ship did not pause, any more than the moon pauses, neither to look nor catch breath. But the soul pauses and holds its breath, for wonder, wonder, which is the very breath of the soul.

20 All the long morning he would be there curled in the wonder of this gulf of creation, where the flying fishes on translucent wings swept in their ecstatic clouds out of the water, in a terror that was brilliant as joy, in a joy brilliant with terror, with wings made of pure water flapping with great speed, and long-shafted bodies of
25 translucent silver like squirts of living water, there in air, brilliant in air, before suddenly they had disappeared, and the blue sea was trembling with a delicate frail surface of green, the still sea lay one moment ahead, untouched, untouched since time began, in its watery loveliness.

30 Sometimes a ship's officer would come and peer over the edge, and look at him lying there. But nothing was said. People didn't like looking over the edge. It was too beautiful, too pure and lovely, the Greater Day. They shoved their snouts a moment over the rail, then withdrew, faintly abashed, faintly sneering, faintly humiliated.
35 After all, they showed snouts, nothing but snouts, to the unbegotten morning, so they might well be humiliated.

Sometimes an island, two islands, three, would show up, dismal and small, with the peculiar American gloom. No land! The soul wanted to see the land. Only the uninterrupted water was purely lovely, pristine.

And the third morning there was a school of porpoises leading   5
the ship. They stayed below surface all the time, so there was no hullabaloo of human staring. Only Gethin Day saw them. And what joy! what joy of life! what marvellous pure joy of being a porpoise within the great sea, of being many porpoises heading and mocking in translucent onrush the menacing, yet futile onrush   10
of a vast ship!

It was a spectacle of the purest and most perfected joy in life that Gethin Day ever saw. The porpoises were ten or a dozen, round-bodied torpedo fish, and they stayed there as if they were not moving, always there, with no motion apparent, under the   15
purely pellucid water, yet speeding on at just the speed of the ship, without the faintest show of movement, yet speeding on in the most miraculous precision of speed. It seemed as if the tail-flukes of the last fish exactly touched the ship's bows, under-water, with the frailest, yet precise and permanent touch. It seemed as if   20
nothing moved, yet fish and ship swept on through the tropical ocean. And the fish moved, they changed places all the time. They moved in a little cloud, and with the most wonderful sport they were above, they were below, they were to the fore, yet all the time the same one speed, the same one speed, and the last fish just   25
touching with his tail-flukes the iron cut-water of the ship. Some would be down in the blue, shadowy, but horizontally motionless in the same speed. Then with a strange revolution, these would be up in pale green water, and others would be down. Even the toucher, who touched the ship, would in a twinkling be changed.   30
And ever, ever the same pure horizontal speed, sometimes a dark back skimming the water's surface light, from beneath, but never the surface broken. And ever the last fish touching the ship, and ever the others speeding in motionless, effortless speed, and intertwining with strange silkiness as they sped, intertwining among   35
one another, fading down to the dark blue shadow, and strangely

emerging again among the silent, swift others, in pale green water. All the time, so swift, they seemed to be laughing.

Gethin Day watched spell-bound, minute after minute, an hour, two hours, and still it was the same, the ship speeding, cutting the water, and the strong-bodied fish heading in perfect balance of speed underneath, mingling among themselves in some strange single laughter of multiple consciousness, giving off the joy of life, sheer joy of life, togetherness in pure complete motion, many lusty-bodied fish enjoying one laugh of life, sheer togetherness, perfect as passion. They gave off into the water their marvellous joy of life, such as the man had never met before. And it left him wonderstruck.

'But they know joy, they know pure joy!' he said to himself in amazement. 'This is the most laughing joy I have ever seen, pure and unmixed. I always thought flowers had brought themselves to the most beautiful perfection in nature. But these fish, these fleshy, warm-bodied fish achieve more than flowers, heading along. This is the purest achievement of joy I have seen in all life: these strong, careless fish. Men have not got in them that secret to be alive together and make one like a single laugh, yet each fish going his own gait. This is sheer joy – and men have lost it, or never accomplished it. The cleverest sportsmen in the world are owls beside these fish. And the togetherness of love is nothing to the spinning unison of dolphins playing under-sea. It would be wonderful to know joy as these fish know it. The life of the deep waters is ahead of us, it contains sheer togetherness and sheer joy. We have never got there.'

There as he leaned over the bowsprit he was mesmerized by one thing only, by joy, by joy of life, fish speeding in water with playful joy. No wonder Ocean was still mysterious, when such red hearts beat in it! No wonder man, with his tragedy, was a pale and sickly thing in comparison! What civilization will bring us to such a pitch of swift laughing togetherness, as these fish have reached?

3 The Atlantic

The ship came in the night to Cuba, to Havana. When she became still, Gethin Day looked out of his port-hole and saw little lights on upreared darkness. Havana!

They went on shore next morning, through the narrow dock-streets near the wharf, to the great boulevard. It was a lovely warm morning, already early December, and the town was in the streets, going to mass, or coming out of the big, unpleasant old churches. The Englishman wandered with the two Danes for an hour or so, in the not very exciting city. Many Americans were wandering around, and nearly all wore badges of some sort. The city seemed, on the surface at least, very American. And underneath, it did not seem to have any very deep character of its own left.

The three men hired a car to drive out and about. The elder of the Danes, a man of about forty-five, spoke fluent colloquial Spanish, learned on the oil-fields of Tampico. 'Tell me,' he said to the chauffeur, 'why do all these *americanos*, these Yankees, wear badges on themselves?'

He spoke, as foreigners nearly always do speak of the Yankees, in a tone of half-spiteful jeering.

'Ah, Señor,' said the driver, with a Cuban grin. 'You know they all come here to drink. They drink so much that they all get lost at night, so they all wear a badge: name, name of hotel, place where it is. Then our policemen find them in the night, turn them over as they lie on the pavement, read name, name of hotel, and place, and so they are put on a cart and carted to home. Ah, the season is only just beginning. Wait a week or two, and they will lie in the streets at night like a battle, and the police doing Red Cross work, carting them to their hotels. Ah, *los americanos!* They are so good. You know they own us now. Yes, they own us. They own Havana. We are a Republic owned by the Americans. *Muy bien,* we give them drink, they give us money. Bah!'

And he grinned with a kind of acrid indifference. He sneered at the whole show, but he wasn't going to do anything about it.

The car drove out to the famous beer-gardens, where all drank beer – then to the inevitable cemetery, which almost rivalled that of New Orleans. 'Every person buried in this cemetery guarantees to put up a tomb-monument costing not less than fifty-thousand dollars.'
5 Then they drove past the new suburb of villas, springing up neat and tidy, spick-and-span, same all the world over. Then they drove out into the country, past the old sugar *haciendas* and to the hills.

And to Gethin Day it was all merely depressing and void of real interest. The Yankees owned it all. It had not much character of its
10 own. And what character it had was the peculiar, dreary character of all America wherever it is a little abandoned. The peculiar gloom of Connecticut or New Jersey, Louisiana or Georgia, a sort of dreariness in the very bones of the land, that shows through immediately the human effort sinks. How quickly the gloom and
15 the inner dreariness of Cuba must have affected the spirit of the Conquistadores, even Columbus!

They drove back to town and ate a really good meal, and watched a stout American couple, apparently man and wife, lunching with a bottle of champagne, a bottle of hock, and a bottle of Burgundy
20 for the two of them, and apparently drinking them all at once. It made one's head reel.

The bright, sunny afternoon they spent on the esplanade by the sea. There the great hotels were still shut. But they had, so to speak, half an eye open: a tea-room going, for example.
25 And Day thought again, how tedious the little day can be! How difficult to spend even one Sunday looking at a city like Havana, even if one has spent the morning driving into the country. The infinite tedium of looking at things! the infinite boredom of things anyhow. Only the rippling, bright, pale-blue sea, and the old fort,
30 gave one the feeling of life. The rest, the great esplanade, the great boulevard, the great hotels, all seemed what they were, dead, dried concrete, concrete, dried deadness.

Everybody was thankful to be back on the ship for dinner, in the dark loneliness of the wharves. See Naples and die. Go seeing any
35 place, and you'll be half dead of exhaustion and tedium by dinner time.

So! good-bye, Havana! The engines were going before breakfast time. It was a bright blue morning. Wharves and harbour slid past, the high bows moved backwards. Then the ship deliberately turned her back on Cuba and the sombre shore, and began to move north, through the blue day, which passed like a sleep. They were moving now into wide space. 5

The next morning they woke to greyness, grey low sky, and hideous low grey water, and a still air. Sandwiched between two greynesses, the long, wicked old ship sped on, as unto death.

'What has happened?' Day asked of one of the officers. 10

'We have come north, to get into the current running east. We come north about the latitude of New York, then we run due east with the stream.'

'What a wicked shame!'

And indeed it was. The sun was gone, the blueness was gone, 15
life was gone. The Atlantic was like a cemetery, an endless, infinite cemetery of greyness, where the bright, lost world of Atlantis is buried. It was December, grey, dark December on a waste of ugly, dead-grey water, under a dead-grey sky.

And so they ran into a swell, a long swell whose oily, sickly waves 20
seemed hundreds of miles long, and travelling in the same direction as the ship's course. The narrow cigar of a ship heaved up the upslope with a nauseating heave, up, up, up, till she righted for a second sickeningly on the top, then tilted, and her screw raced like a dentist's burr in a hollow tooth. Then down she slid, down the 25
long, shivering downslope, leaving all her guts behind her, and the guts of all the passengers too. In an hour, everybody was deathly white, and sicklily grinning, thinking it a sort of joke that would soon be over. Then everybody disappeared, and the game went on: up, up, up, heavingly up, till a pause, ah! – then burr-rr-rr! as 30
the screw came out of water and shattered every nerve. Then whoooosh! the long and awful downrush, leaving the entrails behind.

She was like a plague-ship, everybody disappeared, stewards and everybody. Gethin Day felt as if he had taken poison: and he slept 35

– slept, slept, slept, and yet was all the time aware of the ghastly motion – up, up, up, heavily up, then ah! one moment, followed by the shattering burr-rr-rr! and the unspeakable ghastliness of the downhill slither, where death seemed inside the entrails, and water chattered like the after-death. He was aware of the hour-long moaning, moaning of the Spanish doctor's fat, pale Mexican wife, two cabins away. It went on for ever. Everything went on for ever. Everything was like this for ever, for ever. And he slept, slept, slept, for thirty hours, yet knowing it all, registering just the endless repetition of the motion, the ship's loud squeaking and chirruping, and the ceaseless moaning of the woman.

Suddenly at tea-time the second day he felt better. He got up. The ship was empty. A ghastly steward gave him a ghastly cup of tea, then disappeared. He dozed again, but came to dinner.

They were three people at the long table, in the horribly travelling grey silence: himself, a young Dane, and the elderly, dried Englishwoman. She talked, talked. The three looked in terror at *Sauerkraut* and smoked loin of pork. But they ate a little. Then they looked out on the utterly repulsive, grey, oily, windless night. Then they went to bed again.

The third evening it began to rain, and the motion was subsiding. They were running out of the swell. But it was an experience to remember.

(Unfinished)

Language Notes and Activities

'HER TURN'

Focus
How does this story portray women?

Does it show them in a positive light?

Follow-up
What impression do you get of working-class life and the environment?

What impression do you get of the relationship between Radford and his wife?

List the words that are used to describe Radford and those that are used to describe his wife. What impression does this give of the characters?

What makes the story light-hearted?

What is the significance of the incident in the public house?

truce (3.1): an agreement to stop fighting.
colliers (3.4): coal miners.
prudery (3.4): paying excessive attention to proper social behaviour.
pit (3.8): coal mine.
strike (3.17): stop work as a protest about something.
cajole (3.18): persuade by flattery or by gentle, persistent argument.
entreat (3.18): beg.

Language Notes and Activities

nag (3.18): ask someone to do something in a persistent and annoying way.

strike-pay (3.18): money paid by a Trade Union (see note to 6.13) to its members who are on strike.

publican (3.21): a person who owns or manages a public house (a place where alcoholic drinks are consumed).

Golden Horn (3.22): the name of a public house.

easy-going (3.22): informal; tolerant; relaxed.

crippled (3.23): disabled; made unable to move easily.

rheumatism (3.23): stiffness of the joints or muscles.

bar-parlour (3.24): a sitting-room in a public house.

for dear life (3.25): in a very enthusiastic way; as if one's life depended on it.

Scotch (3.25): whisky.

surveys (3.27): looks carefully or closely at someone or something.

landlady (4.3): a woman who owns or manages a public house.

conundrums (4.9): word puzzles; riddles.

s'll (4.12): shall.

wheer (4.14): where.

under weigh (4.15): being considered.

swarthy (4.16): having a dark complexion.

courting (4.20): spending time together in a romantic relationship.

husky (4.29): throaty; hoarse.

modulated (4.30): altered the tone, volume or pitch of the voice, usually by lowering or softening it.

indolence (4.31): laziness; effortlessness.

carriage (4.32): the way in which someone holds his or her body when walking.

mester (4.33): mister/master; husband.

doin' (4.34): doing.

indifferent (4.35): not showing any interest or concern.

wedlock (5.4): marriage.

fumble (5.12): search clumsily and with difficulty and confusion.

bade (5.18): (from 'to bid') wished.

sleek (5.22): well-groomed and healthy-looking.

dumpling (5.22): someone who is plump.

sly (5.23): crafty.

twang (5.24): nasal quality of the voice that is associated with certain accents.

sleering (5.24): sneering, talking with a sly, suggestive offensiveness.

shirt-sleeves (5.29): not wearing a coat or jacket.

rib (5.32): protrude, stick out (like a rib under the skin).

ha'e (5.34): have.

smite (5.34): small piece.

yi (6.1): yes.

pantry (6.1): a small room or walk-in cupboard where food is kept.

yer (6.2): you are.

comin' (6.2): coming.

jam-tarts (6.4): small pastry cases filled with jam.

tan-tafflins (6.6): a dialect word for jam tarts.

art (6.9): are you.

thinkin' (6.11): thinking.

Union (6.13): Trade Union, an organized association formed to represent workers' interests and protect their rights.

tha's (6.14): you have.

an' (6.14): and.

tha (6.14): you.

mun (6.14): must.

yer (6.15): you.

'aven't (6.15): haven't.

hadna (6.16): had not.

ha'p'ny (6.16): halfpenny, a small, old-fashioned coin.

'appen (6.18): perhaps.

wi' th' (6.19): with the.

shonna (6.21): shall not.

get at (6.23): irritate; annoy.

slack (6.26): not busy; poor.

gangs (6.27): groups.

marbles (6.27): a game that involves rolling small, glass balls along the ground and attempting to hit an opponent's ball.

furnisher-and-upholsterer's shop (6.28–9): a shop selling furniture and other household items. An upholsterer is someone who fits chairs, couches and similar items of furniture with springs, stuffing and covering.

wantin' (6.30): wanting.

shift (6.32): move.

strap (6.34): credit.

linoleum (6.34): a hard-wearing, washable floor-covering.

wringer (6.35): a machine for squeezing water out of wet washing. It consists of two rotating cylinders, turned by a handle, between which the washing is drawn.

breakfast-service (6.35): a set of cups, saucers, plates, etc., used for serving breakfast.

desultory (7.3): disorganized; unmethodical; aimless.

daffodils (7.4): yellow flowers which bloom in the early springtime.

colts (7.4): young male horses.

sithee here (7.6): look here.

betimes (7.11): early; in good time.

th' (7.12): the.

clothes-basket (7.17): a large basket used for holding wet washing.

crockery (7.18): items of household pottery or china such as cups, saucers, plates and bowls.

whativer (7.19): whatever.

hast (7.19): have you.

theer (7.19): there.

'em (7.21): them.

mornin' (7.21): morning.

on th' spend (7.23): spending a lot of money.

seemly (7.23): it seems.

raggy oilcloth (7.27): in this context oilcloth is another name for linoleum. Raggy means ragged and worn.

carter (7.30): someone who uses a cart in order to transport goods.

gi'e (7.34): give.

slouching (7.35): careless; casual; extremely relaxed.

corker (8.5): something particularly striking or special.

mangle (8.6): the same as a wringer (see first note to 6.35), a machine for squeezing water out of wet washing.

dost (8.7): do you.

tha'd (8.9): you would.

ha'e ter (8.9): have to.

officiously (8.12): in an interfering way.

thrippence (8.13): three pennies.

thysen (8.14): yourself.

half-a-crown (8.15): an old-fashioned coin worth two shillings and sixpence (12½p).

tipped (8.16): gave someone money above what was owed for a service they had performed.

array (8.17): large amount; an impressive or striking group of things.

winder (8.19): something that shocks or amazes; something that takes the breath away.

copper (8.24): penny.

i' th' (8.24): in the.

smug (8.27): self-satisfied; conceited.

clenched (8.29): gripped tightly; firmly closed.

half-sovereign (9.1): an old-fashioned coin, no longer used, that was worth about ten shillings (50p). A sovereign was worth about one pound sterling.

'ODOUR OF CHRYSANTHEMUMS'

Focus

How does this story present the relationship between men and women?

What impression do you get of Elizabeth and Walter Bates? Does this impression change as the story progresses?

Follow-up

How is the story presented? Are you asked to sympathize with any of the characters?

Why and how are chrysanthemums symbolic?

Language Notes and Activities

Pick out all the phrases used to describe the industrial environment. What impression does it give you of the landscape and how the narrator feels about it?

How and why is tension built up in the story?

Do Elizabeth's feelings change after her husband is found dead? If so, in what ways and why?

Explain the significance of the phrase, 'There had been nothing between them.'

locomotive engine (10.1): railway engine.

waggons (10.2): (normally 'wagons') wheeled vehicles that are used for carrying heavy loads.

colt (10.3): a young male horse.

gorse (10.4): a shrub that has yellow flowers and thick green spines.

raw (10.4): cold and harsh.

canter (10.5): the smooth, easy, medium pace of a horse, slower than a gallop but faster than a trot.

footplate (10.7): the part of a railway engine from which the driver operates the controls.

trucks (10.8): the same as wagons, wheeled vehicles used for transporting heavy loads.

coppice (10.11): a group of trees.

hips (10.12): the fleshy fruit of a wild or cultivated rose.

spinney (10.13): a small wooded area.

cleaved (10.14): clung closely to.

whimsey (10.16): a pool of water near a mine, originally used to supply water for steam-powered winding engines.

fowls (10.16): hens; chickens.

alders (10.17): an alder is a type of tree.

roost (10.17): to sleep for the night.

stagnant (10.19): still; unmoving.

headstocks (10.20): part of the machinery that is noticeable on the surface of the mine. It is connected with the raising and lowering of miners into the mine.

colliery (10.21): coal mine.

winding-engine (10.22): a machine for lifting.

turned up (10.23): returned to the surface.

sidings (11.2): short railway tracks that connect with the main track.

cinder (11.3): a small piece of burnt coal.

stooping (11.9): bending.

apron (11.12): a protective garment worn over the front of the clothes to keep them clean while working.

of imperious mien (11.13): having a haughty and authoritative bearing.

brook course (11.16): the route followed by a small stream.

brook (11.24): a small stream.

raspberry-canes (11.25): the long woody stems of raspberry plants.

taciturn (11.33): uncommunicative; reserved.

refrained (12.4): stopped doing something.

wan (12.5): pale.

bay of lines (12.9): an area of railway lines.

hearty (12.15): enthusiastic and cheerful.

mash (12.16): make a drink of tea.

winced (12.21): made an expression of pain with the face because of seeing or thinking something embarrassing or unpleasant.

censure (12.25): criticism; expression of disapproval.

coaxingly (12.26): gently persuading.

hearth (12.28): the floor of a fireplace, especially that which extends out into the room.

engine-cab (12.32): the driver's compartment in a railway engine.

'a' (12.35): have.

an' (12.35): and.

bout (13.2): a time spent doing something, in this context, drinking is meant; a fit of drunkenness.

heered (13.4): heard.

Lord Nelson (13.4): the name of a public house.

braggin' (13.4): bragging; boasting.

b— (13.5): indicating a swear word.

afore (13.5): before.

half a sovereign (13.5): an old-fashioned coin, no longer used, that was worth about ten shillings (50p). A sovereign was worth about one pound sterling.

Sat'day (13.7): Saturday.

aye (13.10): yes.

settler (13.14): something that reduces you to silence: a 'finisher'; a conclusive argument.

sombre (13.18): serious and melancholy.

fender (13.24): a metal guard built on to the front of an open fire that prevents coals from falling out.

pertinacity (13.31): determination.

occupied by her husband (13.32): her husband was in her thoughts and taking up all her attention.

took the potatoes to strain (13.35): removed the cooking water from the potatoes.

drain (14.2): a channel or pipe which takes away waste water.

hob (14.8): a flat metal surface, level with the top of the fire grate, used for heating pans.

batter pudding (14.8): a pudding made from a mixture of flour, eggs, milk and water, and baked in an oven.

chid (14.14): scolded; told off.

wistful (14.21): sad; yearning.

'cos (14.23): because.

Prince o' Wales (14.26): Prince of Wales, the name of a public house.

piteously (14.27): deserving pity; in a way that brings out feelings of pity.

ripping (14.32): part of the coal mining process involving taking down the roof of an underground road in order to make it higher.

moving a thick piece of bread before the fire (14.36–15.1): toasting a piece of bread in front of an open fire.

fair (15.6): quite; rather.

mending (15.7): putting more coal on.

wafflin' (15.14): waffling, waving or flapping.

so's (15.14): so as.

'er (15.14): her.

crozzled up (15.23): curled or shrivelled up with heat; overcooked and burnt.

canna (15.29): cannot.

dustpan (15.31): a small shovel used for removing ashes from, or adding fresh coal to, a fire.

good gracious (15.35): an expression of annoyance.

maternity (16.4): pregnancy; expecting a baby.

lamp glass (16.7): a glass cover placed over the wick of an oil or gas lamp to protect and control the flame.

copper reflector (16.7): a piece of copper in the lamp that re-directs the flame.

goodness me (16.11): an expression of annoyance.

afire (16.12): on fire.

stick (16.36): stay; remain.

pit-dirt (16.36): the dirt and coal dust that miners are covered in after working down the coal mine. Pit is another word for a coal mine.

slink (17.3): move in a furtive and secretive way.

wrath (17.7): great anger.

singlet (17.9): an undergarment, a sleeveless, thick vest.

flannel (17.9): a type of soft, cotton cloth.

quailed (17.14): trembled.

suspended (17.14): stopped temporarily.

sleepers (17.15): wooden cross-beams that support the rails on a railway track.

hush (17.16): be quiet.

waggon of slippers (17.19–20): a small box on wheels containing soft, indoor shoes.

inarticulate (17.22): unable to speak.

survey (17.26): look closely at.

suspense bristled in the room (17.27–8): this phrase means that suspense was evident in the room, so much so that it almost made the hairs on their necks stand up.

plaintively (17.30): sadly.

primed (17.31): prepared; provided.

flannel (17.36): in this context, a small cloth that is used for washing the hands and face.

tinged (18.10): slightly mixed with.

stairfoot door (18.12): a door at the bottom of the stairs.

bulked with (18.16): filled with; massed with.

stile (18.20): a step or set of steps that enables people to climb over a fence, wall or hedge.

faltered (18.27): hesitated; became unsure.

scullery (19.1): a small room where dishes and pans are washed and stored, and where other kitchen chores, such as preparing vegetables, are done.

master (19.5): husband.

'asn't 'e (19.7): hasn't he.

'ome (19.7): home.

'ad (19.7): had.

'is (19.7): his.

'e's (19.8): he's.

'alf (19.8): half.

nothink (19.12): nothing.

mester (19.13): mister/master; husband.

anythink (19.18): anything.

th' (19.21): the.

childer (19.21): children.

remonstrance (19.23): a protest.

frocks (19.25): dresses.

squab (19.26): couch; sofa.

black American cloth (19.27): oilcloth, a waterproof covering for tables, chairs etc.

slops (19.28): spilled liquid or tea dregs.

shawl (19.31): a square of fabric worn by women over their shoulders or their head and shoulders.

shanna (19.33): shall not.

litter (20.1): objects that have been scattered about untidily.

tattooing (20.6): designs made on the skin by pricking and staining it with permanent dye.

'asna (20.7): hasn't.

whoam (20.7): home.

yit (20.7): yet.

wheer (20.8): where.

non (20.9): not.

ower theer (20.9): over there.

'appen (20.11): perhaps.

Yew (20.11): the name of a public house.

'im (20.14): him.

finishin' (20.14): finishing.

stint (20.14): a fixed period of time.

Loose-all (20.14): the signal to finish work.

bin (20.14): been.

com'n (20.15): came.

are ter comin' (20.15–16): are you coming.

but (20.16): only.

a'ef a minnit (20.16–17): half a minute.

ter (20.17): to.

thinkin' (20.17): thinking.

wor (20.18): was.

behint (20.18): behind.

'ud (20.18): would.

i' th' (20.18): in the.

bantle (20.18): batch or group.

perplexed (20.19): puzzled; troubled.

fretted (20.23): worried; agitated.

deplored (20.25): regretted.

taking liberties (20.27): behaving inappropriately towards someone; being too familiar with someone.

entry (20.30): a narrow passage or tunnel in between houses.

mind (20.34): be careful.

Ah've (20.34): I have.

Ah'd (20.34): I would.

ruts (20.35): grooves or channels, often made by wheels, but in this context a rough, uneven surface is suggested.

sumb'dy (20.35): somebody.

breakin' (20.35): breaking.

dunna (21.3): do not.

butty (21.6): a contractor or a superior workman in charge of a team of miners.

chuff (21.12): a word imitating the noise of the machinery.

deputy (21.16): the person responsible for safety measures in a coal mine. The 'nine o'clock deputy' would be going down for the night shift.

rebuking (21.16): telling off; scolding; reprimanding.

working myself up (21.20): becoming very worried, preoccupied and concerned.

s'll (21.21): shall.

peevishly (21.27): irritably; in a complaining way.

vexed (21.34): irritated.

sittin' (22.17): sitting.

wi' (22.19): with.

knowin' (22.23): knowing.

pension (22.28): in this context, a fixed amount paid at regular intervals as compensation for the loss of her husband.

tiresome (22.30): annoying; causing weariness.

spare (23.5): save.

mend his ways (23.6): be a better person.

skirr (23.12): make a whirring sound.

make allowances (23.18): take things into consideration; take a more kindly view towards.

bringin' (23.26): bringing.

lamp-cabin (23.31): a small hut or shed where the miners' lamps are stored.

butties (24.5): see note to 21.6.

o' (24.5): of.

atop 'n 'im (24.6): on top of him.

widow (24.7): a woman whose husband is dead.

face (24.8): the working area in the coal mine.

niver (24.9): never.

smothered (24.9): suffocated; deprived of air.

parlour (24.18): a living room in the house, but one usually kept for special occasions and not used every day.

lustre-glasses (24.23): vases with an opalescent, metallic glaze.

chiffonier (24.28): a low cabinet or cupboard with shelves above.

dresser (24.32): a piece of furniture comprising a set of drawers or cupboards with a set of shelves above.

to air (24.33): to expose to warm air in order to remove dampness.

rocker (24.36): rocking-chair.

pantry (25.2): a small room or walk-in cupboard in which food is stored.

penthouse (25.3): a shed with a sloping roof built against the outer wall of a building.

collier (25.10): coal miner.

stretcher (25.11): a device made from a piece of material stretched across a frame and used for carrying someone who is sick, injured or dead.

lintel (25.13): a horizontal beam of wood that supports the weight of a wall above a door.

mind now (25.26): be careful.

duster (25.33): a piece of cloth used for removing dust, especially from furniture and other household objects.

'sphyxiated (26.6): asphyxiated; suffocated.

o' (26.7): on.

the horror of the thing bristled (26.12): again 'bristled' is used to suggest that the horror is very evident, making the hairs on the back of the neck stand up.

fuss (26.25): commotion; protest; complaint.

bade (27.3): told.

sh–sh (27.3): hush; be quiet.

lay him out (27.17): prepare the body for burial.

clammy (27.19): unpleasantly damp and cold.

countermanded (27.27): as if given an instruction to cancel a previous instruction.

inviolable (27.27): secure; safe from violence or attack.

impregnable (27.36): unable to be touched by any outside influence.

ministered (28.7): performed certain duties for.

sibilant (28.23): hissing.

unavailing (28.27): useless; of no benefit or help.

ha' (28.34): have.
made his peace (28.34): confessed his sins and become reconciled with God.
rigid (30.3): stiff.
reparation (30.5): amends; compensation for a wrong.
next world (30.10): the place to which those who have died go, heaven in this context.
the beyond (30.11): the place to which those who have died go, heaven in this context.
inert (30.31): not moving; still.
lest (30.36): for fear that.

'YOU TOUCHED ME'

Focus
Describe Hadrian's impact on the Rockley family.

What points are made about social class in the story?

Follow-up
What impression do you gain of the Rockley family and their environment before Hadrian's return?

What is Emmie's attitude to Hadrian? Why do you think she displays this attitude?

Why do you think Hadrian hates England?

Why does Mr Rockley want the marriage to take place?

Pick out all the words and phrases which are used to describe the following characters: Emmie, Matilda, Mr Rockley, Hadrian. What does this tell you about the characters?

Do you think that this is a realistic story? Give reasons for and against.

What point do you think Lawrence is making in this story?

girt in (32.1): surrounded by.

pottery (32.2): a factory where pots (cups, plates, bowls, etc.) are made.

privet (32.3): an evergreen shrub often used in hedges.

outhouses (32.7): small buildings or sheds situated near a main building.

crates (32.10): large, open boxes used for carrying and storing objects.

drays (32.12): large horse-drawn carts used for carrying heavy loads.

lasses (32.13): girls; young women.

overalls (32.13): protective garments worn over the clothes to keep them clean.

larked (32.15): had fun; laughed and joked.

spatter (32.23): splash.

silt (32.23): spread.

premises (32.23): land and buildings.

old maids (32.26): an unflattering and offensive description of women who are not married.

have expectations above the common (32.27–33.1): think that they deserve better than ordinary people.

colliers (33.3): coal miners.

pottery-hands (33.3): people who work in a pottery.

not to be sneezed at (33.6): an opportunity that is not to be ignored.

proletariat (33.8): the working class; the lower classes in society.

nonconformist (33.8): belonging to a Protestant church which does not adhere to the doctrine and practices of the Church of England.

Mary . . . Martha (33.13): a reference to the New Testament of the Christian Bible (Luke 10, 38–42). Mary preferred to sit and listen to Jesus, while Martha was busy cooking and cleaning.

accomplishments (33.16): skills or talents.

looked up to (33.16): respected.

melancholy (33.18): sad.

racket (33.28): loud noise.

Language Notes and Activities

In all this ointment there was one little fly (33.30): 'a fly in the ointment' means that there is one small thing that is wrong.

Charity Institution (33.33–4): an orphanage; a home for children whose parents have died and who have no family to look after them.

prodigy (33.35): something extraordinary, inexplicable or marvellous.

cockney (34.3): a London dialect.

being sprung on (34.4): being introduced without warning.

jeering (34.7): scornful; mocking.

complied (34.9): agreed to do what was wanted.

laconic (34.16): using very few words.

sly (34.18): crafty; lacking honesty; cunning.

cautious (34.18): showing carefulness and thoughtfulness; guarded and cagey.

tacitly (34.19): in a way that is implied but is not spoken of openly.

akin (34.20): alike; similar in some way; related.

thrust upon (34.26): imposed upon; forced upon.

played truant (34.27): was absent from school without permission.

badge (34.28): school emblem and identification.

raking off (34.29): running off.

Colonies (34.32): this refers to the countries that were part of the former British Empire and were ruled by Britain. These countries included Australia, Canada and South Africa. Many people emigrated from Britain to these countries at the time the story was written.

pang (35.2): a feeling of emotion.

queer (35.3): strange.

dropsy (35.9): a disease involving an abnormal build-up of fluid.

armistice (35.10): the truce that ended the First World War. It became effective on 11 November 1918.

leave (35.10): official time off from duty in the army.

fluttered (35.12): nervous; agitated; thrown into confusion.

trying (35.16): difficult.

morning-room (35.19): a sitting-room that is used in the mornings.

turned up (35.22): arrived.

bobbed up (35.23): pinned up in curls.

stair-rods (35.24): pieces of wood or metal which hold stair carpet in place.

drawing-room (35.25): a formal room in a house usually used for entertaining guests.

lather (35.26): soapy foam or froth.

coquettishly (35.27): frivolously; flirtatiously.

mortification (35.28): shame and humiliation.

self-possessed (35.28-9): confident and in control of feelings and emotions.

kit-bag (35.29): a large cylindrical canvas bag for holding military clothing and equipment.

wringing (35.34): wiping.

got off (35.36): was able to leave.

fancy (36.1): an expression expressing surprise.

partridge (36.12): a bird that is hunted for sport and for food.

cover (36.13): hiding place.

midst (36.19): middle.

propped up (36.22): supported; leaning.

whence (36.23): where.

resplendent (36.23): having an impressive appearance.

ablaze (36.24): bright, as if on fire. The blooming tulips suggest that it is springtime, so it is likely that the trees are 'ablaze' with blossom.

puffed him up (36.25): made him swollen.

wreck (36.27): the broken-down remains.

sheepishly (36.30): in an embarrassed and awkward way.

life-guardsman (36.31): the Life Guards are a cavalry regiment in the British Army and are well known for the tallness of the soldiers.

altered (37.3): changed.

sotto voce (37.3): in a soft voice so as not to be overheard.

grimace (37.5): a facial expression showing disgust.

cocky (37.7): arrogant; confident.

mannie (37.9): a small man, usually used affectionately to describe young boys, but here used sarcastically.

new-fledged (37.9): newly acquired.

cocksure (37.10): arrogantly confident; very sure of yourself.

legacy (37.23): money or property that is left to someone in a will.

basin (37.27): bowl.

pallor (37.30): pale complexion.

rouge (37.30): reddish make-up used to add colour to the cheeks.

cronies (38.1): close friends.

common (38.15): vulgar; lower class.

confab (38.15): casual discussion; chat.

rare (38.17): unusually great; very much.

sauntering (38.26): strolling casually; walking unhurriedly.

churlishly (38.31): in a surly, grumpy and sullen way.

khaki (38.32): brownish yellow fabric used for making military uniforms.

plebeian (38.34): relating to ordinary people, especially those of the lower classes.

declaimed against (38.35): spoke forcefully against.

propertied classes (38.35): upper classes of society; people who have money and property.

rebuked (39.2): criticized; told off sharply.

jersey (39.16): sweater; woollen pullover.

haggard (39.29): tired-looking.

watch and chain (39.36): a pocket watch and the chain to which it is attached.

tranced (40.7): in a dazed, hypnotic state and unaware of what is going on around you.

clairvoyant (40.8): a psychic person, someone who is supposedly able to see things beyond the range of normal human perception.

entranced (40.15): in a dazed, hypnotic state and unaware of what is going on around you.

started (40.33): moved in a sudden way.

reason (41.10): justify; explain.

aloof (41.18): remote in manner; unwilling to become involved with other people.

at bay (41.18): at a point where there is no escape, especially when being hunted.

borne (41.24): tolerated; endured.

quenched (41.26): put out; subdued.

alert (41.30): alive; in a way that is prepared and lively.

reticent (41.31): unwilling to communicate; reluctant.

high-bred (41.36): of good birth, aristocratic.

tapering (42.2): elegant, long, slender and gradually becoming slimmer towards the end.

ringed (42.3): wearing rings.

schemed (42.6): made a secret and cunning plan.

commonplace (42.13): ordinary.

restive (43.2): uneasy.

inscrutably (43.7): in a way that is difficult to interpret because there is no obvious expression.

flushed (43.14): went red in the face.

abated (43.24): became less.

raving (43.30): mad; insane.

dumbfounded (43.35): unable to speak because of astonishment.

sound (44.10): acceptable; worthy of approval.

testily (44.10): in an annoyed way; impatiently.

clear out (44.11): go away.

malevolent (44.14): as if wanting to cause harm.

gripped (44.17): took hold of.

delirious (44.19): irrational, out of one's mind because of illness.

solicitor (44.23): lawyer.

sliving (44.30): scheming, crafty, cunning.

out of his mind (44.31): mad; insane.

pottering about (45.15): wandering about aimlessly, dawdling.

barred (45.25): blocked.

guttersnipe (45.34): a rough and vulgar person, especially one from the lower classes.

drawn up (46.10): prepared.

wholly (46.11): totally, entirely.

held good (46.11): remained valid.

mute (46.20): silent.

indomitable (46.24): brave; determined.

pointing (46.26): indicating.

stoical (47.30): showing patience and endurance.
unyielding (47.31): not giving in.
pondered (47.31): thought deeply.
withdrawal (48.1): going back.
without avail (48.1–2): without success.
decent (48.15): acceptable; conforming to accepted standards.
come round (49.6): finally agreed; changed your mind.
twinkling (49.7): sparkling.
flew abroad (49.10): was widely known.
nipped (49.11): touched.
registrar (49.15): a person who performs and authorizes civil marriages.
round the gills (49.18): in the face.

THE FOX

Focus
How does the narrator portray each of the characters?

Is there anything to suggest that we should sympathize with one character more than another?

What are the implications of the way in which the characters are portrayed?

How does this affect your view of the ending of the story?

Follow-up
Describe the relationship between: (a) March and the fox; (b) March and Henry; (c) March and Banford; (d) Banford and Henry.

How is the fox linked to Henry?

Describe the ways in which D. H. Lawrence uses colour in the story.

Why do you think that Banford has to die? Is she the villain of the story?

poultry (50.4): chickens and hens.

beasts (50.5): cattle; cows.

principal investor (50.7): the person putting the most money into a business.

tradesman (50.8): a man involved in trade, especially a shopkeeper.

carpentry and joinery (50.11): making things out of wood.

Leghorns . . . Plymouths . . . Wyandottes (50.20): types of chicken.

heifers (50.21): young cows.

closes (50.22): land belonging to the farm.

chagrin (51.3): a feeling of humiliation and disappointment.

coops (51.7): enclosures for hens.

appurtenances (51.7): accompanying parts of something.

exacting (51.12): extremely hard; requiring great effort.

puttees (51.15): strips of cloth wound round the lower part of the leg from ankle to knee.

breeches (51.15): trousers, especially those that reach down only to the knee.

indifference (51.18): lack of interest or care.

sardonic (51.21): disdainful; mocking.

obnoxious (51.25): offensive; unpleasant.

languid (51.36): lacking energy; slow moving.

foraging (52.1): searching for food.

war conditions (52.5): this refers to the general lack of goods owing to the First World War (1914–18).

Daylight Saving Bill (52.6): it was adopted in 1916 as a war-time measure and involved advancing the clocks by one hour in order to make better use of the hours of daylight.

curvilinear (52.14): curved.

fire-screen (52.15): a decorative screen placed in front of a fireplace when the fire is not lit.

whims (52.16): sudden impulses.

homestead (52.20): a house, particularly a farmhouse, together with its outbuildings and land.

sentinel (52.28): guard; sentry.

nervous (53.1): liable to suffer from stress and emotional agitation.

magnanimity (53.2–3): generosity.

solitude (53.3): the state of being alone.

despondent (53.8): very unhappy.

the White Horse (53.11): a huge white horse is cut into the chalk of Uffington Hill near Wantage, Berkshire, in the south of England.

circumvent (53.19): avoid; outwit; get round a barrier or restriction.

brush (53.20): a fox's tail.

ruddy (53.20): red-coloured.

musing (53.25): gazing dreamily.

rapt (53.27): completely involved in or fascinated by; concentrating completely on something and ignoring everything else.

spell-bound (54.6): in a state where all attention and interest is held completely as if under a magical power.

daunted (54.8): anxious; discouraged; intimidated.

pursed (54.14): drew the lips together so that they wrinkle and form a circle.

pertinaciously (54.17): in a determined and resolute way.

hither and thither (54.22): here and there.

roost (54.26): a place where birds sleep at night.

unabashed (55.3): not ashamed or embarrassed.

muzzle (55.6): an animal's nose and mouth.

contemptuous (55.7–8): showing strong dislike or lack of respect towards someone or something.

damsons (56.10): small fruits similar to plums.

spell (56.15): magical influence.

desolate (56.31): solitary; joyless.

tramps (56.32): people without homes who travel around on foot, often begging for a living.

lest (56.32): in case.

physique (56.34): body.

sodden (57.1): very wet.

dismal (57.2): depressing.

crochet-work (57.8): crochet is a form of needle-work used to make clothes or decorative items. Wool or cotton is used and the yarn is looped through itself with a special hook to form stitches.

lowing (57.13): the noise made by cows; mooing.

recoiled (57.17): drew back.

kit (57.29): equipment.

down (58.9): very soft, fine hairs.

dilated (58.13): widened.

ay (58.26): yes.

baffled (58.30): confused.

Salonika (59.7): a Greek port.

lamely (59.9): inadequately.

Swan (59.11): the name of a public house.

presence of mind (59.20): calmness; decisiveness.

primmed up (59.33–4): tightened up; set firmly.

puckering (59.34): wrinkling.

racked her brain (60.2): thought hard.

larder (60.4): a small, cool room or large cupboard used for storing food.

arrested by her (60.13): held by her.

unremitting (61.7): continuing; persisting.

perky (61.9): lively.

voraciously (61.10): hungrily.

Cornish (61.18): from Cornwall, a county in the south-west of England.

acute (61.24): sensitive.

capital (61.33): money that is invested.

landworkers (61.36): during the First World War, women were employed as farm hands.

plangent (62.4): resonant; deep and rich.

tickled (62.18): amused.

yap (62.31): high, barking sound.

courteous (63.3): polite.

dwindled (63.21): grew less and less.

influenza (63.27): a widespread illness producing a high temperature, sore throat, runny nose, dry cough and muscle pain.

propriety (63.33): socially correct and proper behaviour.

naïveté (64.1): in a simple, unsophisticated way.

courtesy (64.19): politeness.

gratification (64.27): satisfaction.

luxuriated in (64.29): obtained great enjoyment from.

seared (65.8): burned or scorched.

hospitable (65.13): friendly, welcoming and generous towards visitors.

curvature of the spine (65.17): a condition in which the spine becomes curved, with sufferers having the appearance of a rounded, hunched back.

insatiable (65.22): impossible to satisfy.

draw-pump (65.28): a device for moving or raising water.

soft-water cistern (65.28): an underground tank for collecting rainwater.

dilapidated (65.30): in a condition of disrepair or decay.

keep (66.4): food and a place to stay.

flu (66.15): an abbreviation of 'influenza' (see note to 63.27).

Plough and Harrow (66.16): the name of a public house.

billeted (66.18): given temporary accommodation in the villagers' homes.

exultant (67.15): triumphant; joyful or very happy.

pellucid (67.19): clear; transparent.

board (68.5): an amount of money paid in exchange for food and a place to stay.

piqued (68.16): stimulated.

elate (68.17): happy.

impelled (68.21): forced; made to go.

acquiescence (68.32): passive agreement to something rather than expressing approval or support.

vulnerable (68.35): exposed to emotional or physical hurt.

subtly (68.35): indirectly, not obviously.

tomfoolery (69.8): silly or foolish behaviour.

quarry (69.21): an animal or bird that is hunted by someone or something.

mesmerism (69.22): a form of hypnotism; the ability to fascinate someone or hold their attention in such a way that is almost hypnotic.

profound (69.25): intense.

to the true pitch (69.28): to the greatest extent.

volition (69.32): using your will to make a decision or to choose something.

regiment (69.35): a large unit of soldiers.

fortnight (70.4): two weeks.

trestle (70.7): a supporting framework that consists of a horizontal plank held up by a pair of splayed legs at each end.

mistress of herself (70.20): in control of her feelings.

transfixed (70.24): momentarily unable to move.

imperceptibly (71.2): slightly.

transient (71.12): lasting only a short time.

swoon (71.20): faint.

exultance (71.25): extreme happiness.

phosphorescent (71.29): emitting light; glowing.

hysteria (72.9): an extremely nervous state in which someone loses control of his or her emotions and becomes unstable.

disconsolately (72.26): miserably.

scraper (72.33): a metal frame across which the soles of dirty boots and shoes are wiped in order to clean mud from them.

scones (73.2): small cakes made from flour, fat and milk.

nettled (73.21): irritated; annoyed.

suave (73.22): charming and polite.

twanging (73.29): having a nasal quality.

rude (73.32): impolite; disrespectful.

ejaculated (73.34): exclaimed.

unheeding (74.3): not noticing; not responding.

Captain Mayne Reid (74.20): Thomas Mayne Reid (1818–83) was an Anglo-Irish novelist who wrote adventure stories set in North America, Africa and the South Seas.

lumber-camp (74.27): a temporary living place (huts or tents) for people who cut down trees.

Turkey rug (74.28): a hand-woven woollen floor-covering that is richly coloured and has a deep pile.

tremulously (74.32): in a trembling, quivering way.

grate (74.33): a metal frame that holds the coal or wood in a fire.

spasmodically (75.5): at irregular intervals.

fidgety (75.14): not able to remain still.

malignant (75.26): harmful; cruel.

a penny for them (75.28): 'a penny for your thoughts', a phrase or saying meaning, tell me what you are thinking about.

shrewish (77.2): bad-tempered.

jumpy (77.23): anxious.

nervy (77.23): uneasy.

jump (78.13): move quickly and suddenly when frightened or surprised.

fretfully (79.34): in a bad-tempered or sad way because one is unhappy and worried.

every fibre (80.2–3): every part.

scathed (80.10): as if damaged by blasting or scorching.

insidiously (80.14): harmfully and destructively, but in an indirect way.

stock (80.19): farm animals.

gloating (81.17): expressing delight at one's own good luck; smug and self-satisfied.

plaintive (81.23): sad-sounding, especially in a weak and complaining way.

impertinence (81.25): disrespect, impudence and rudeness, especially to someone who is older.

fixity (81.32): in a fixed and unchanging state.

uncouthly (82.14–15): in a way that shows a lack of politeness.

composure (82.22): calmness of mind and behaviour.

chimney-pot (82.27): a short pipe placed on the top of a hollow vertical structure that allows smoke from the fire to escape.

stalked out (82.29): walked away in a stiff, angry and proud fashion.

supercilious (83.2): full of arrogance and contempt.

intonation (83.6): pitch of the voice.

antagonists (83.8): enemies; opponents.

complacency (83.9): self-satisfied to the extent that one is not concerned with any possible worries or dangers.

yelping (83.18): making a sudden, short, sharp barking sound.

stealthily (83.21): in a slow, secretive way so as to avoid being noticed.

boomerang (83.36): a flat, curved piece of wood which is designed to return to the person who throws it. It is used as a weapon by the Australian Aborigines.

your own lookout (84.7): your own problem or concern.

labourer (84.21): a person who does manual work.

stifled (85.10): tried to stop from being heard.

grove (85.30): a small group of trees.

hullabaloo (86.7): a lot of noise and fuss.

farmstead (86.9): the farmhouse and its surrounding buildings and land.

crawk (86.19): a word imitating the sound made by the chickens.

reverberating (87.2): echoing.

quark-quarking (87.7): a word imitating the sound made by the ducks.

fleece (87.23): an animal's coat.

dog-fox (88.18): male fox.

spatula (89.3): a flat, flexible kitchen utensil with a handle. It is used for lifting and spreading.

nonchalant (89.30): unconcerned and calm.

crucified (89.32): executed by being nailed to a cross.

contrivance (90.4–5): device or machine.

clear out (90.25): leave.

petulantly (91.5): in a bad-tempered and sulky way.

hoax (91.7): a trick or joke; an act of deception.

jammed up (91.26): crushed; squeezed.

steerage (91.26): the cheapest passenger accommodation in a ship.

pertinently (92.6): relevantly; in a way that was connected to what was under consideration.

got into league with (92.11): made secret plans with.

hot bottle (92.18): a container filled with hot water and placed in a bed in order to warm it.

cub (92.25): a young fox.

cogitating (92.25): thinking deeply.

convulsed (92.29): so filled with emotion that it causes one to shake.

thwarted (92.30): prevented from doing something.

tension (92.35): a nervous, anxious or aggressive situation.

tam-o'-shanter hat (93.3): a brimless woollen hat with a bobble at the middle of the crown.

toiling (93.18): moving slowly and with difficulty.

tunic (93.21): a loose outer garment, often without sleeves.

solicitude (93.23): anxious care and concern.

robust (94.7): healthy, vigorous and strong.

cheap (94.22): not valued; not deserving of respect.

make a mug of (94.26): make a fool of.

I wouldn't be in your shoes (94.28–9): I would not want to be in your position.

acid (95.23): bitter; unkind and critical.

chiffon (96.11): a thin, transparent fabric.

frailty (96.12): physical weakness.

crape (96.25): a light, fine fabric.

land girl (96.33): a female farm worker.

mucky (96.34): dirty.

piggled with (97.10–11): picked at.

patent (97.23): leather with a hard, shiny finish.

hard-cloth (97.26): a coarse or stiff fabric.

squirm (97.32): feel uncomfortable.

breaks my dream (98.6–7): said of an event which happens during the day that reminds you of a dream from the previous night.

chubbed (99.11): pleasantly plump.

try his throw (99.12–13): make his attempt or challenge.

made [her] blood boil (99.21): made her very angry.

slippers (99.32): soft, indoor shoes.

turtled up (99.34): reacted with anger and indignation.

fighting cock (99.35): a male fowl that is bred and trained to fight.

rug (100.2): a blanket or thick cover.

spasm (100.9): a sudden, uncontrollable action.

attend (101.7): take notice.

old age pensions (103.24): in this context, old age pensioners, people who receive regular sums of money from the state because they no longer work, as they are too old.

harp on (103.28): keep talking about something so much that it becomes annoying.

enigmatic (103.34): mysterious; difficult to understand.

clamorous (104.12): loud and insistent in demanding attention.

to repent it (105.6–7): to regret it.

divined (105.20): sensed.

names stuck up (105.30): a notice pinned up in a registrar's office declaring an intention to marry. It is a legal requirement that couples, before marriage, should publicly declare their intentions in order for any objections to be raised.

Salisbury plains (106.2): there was a large army training camp on Salisbury Plain, an area of rolling, chalky downland in the south of England where Stonehenge is located.

chubby (106.4): pleasantly plump.

forlorn (106.14): unhappy and lonely.

blind (106.26): make it difficult to understand; confuse.

grounds (106.34): reason; basis.

delicate (107.7): frail; weak; likely to suffer from ill-health.

screws loose . . . softening of the brain . . . off my chump (107.11, 17): all phrases suggesting madness, insanity, mental illness.

lunatic asylum (107.19): a hospital for those who are mentally ill.

cry the whole thing off (107.25): withdraw from the arrangement.

balked (108.4): prevented from carrying out a plan.

lurking (108.10): furtively plotting.

issue (108.10): outcome, result.

affairs (108.16): business; things that have to be attended to.

suppression (108.16–17): conscious avoidance of thoughts and feelings.

one thorn rankled (108.18): one thing caused bitter and angry feelings.

leave of absence (108.23): an official permission to be absent from the army.

Captain (108.25): an army officer.

canteen (108.28): a place where food is served.

no business (109.5): no right.

what's afoot (109.12): what's happening.

for God's sake (109.20): an expression used to emphasize what is being said.

gin and bitters (109.23): a drink consisting of gin mixed with a slightly alcoholic liquid flavoured with plant extracts.

firing (109.35): wood for the fire.

yawning (110.4): wide; gaping.

bowler hat (110.21): a hard, felt hat with a narrow brim and a round crown.

spelch (110.32): small piece.

rickety (111.3): in a bad condition; likely to fall down.

craned (111.24): stretched the neck in order to see something better.

pommel (113.5): the end of a handle.

axe-shaft (113.32): the handle of an axe.

drake (114.14): a male duck.

stemming (114.14): coming.

cockling (114.15): wobbling.

Spanish Armada (114.18): this refers to the Spanish invasion fleet that was defeated by the British in 1588.

waggled (114.26): moved with a wobbling, shaking motion.

gondolas (114.27–8): narrow, flat-bottomed boats used on the canals in Venice.

soberly (115.11): seriously.

tree felling (115.18): cutting down trees.

bough (115.28): the branch of a tree.

winged (115.33): injured; wounded superficially.

petrified (116.8): completely still because of fear.

grizzle (116.22): cry in a quiet but persistent way.

peaked (117.25): pale.

submergence (117.31): in a state of being kept under.

made his brow go black (117.35): made him angry or annoyed.

fibrils (118.4): long, slender threads.

well-being (118.18): a healthy, happy and comfortable state.

verily (118.19): in truth; truly.

sphere (118.21): area of influence, interests and activities.

goal (118.35): the object or aim that you want to achieve.

catastrophic (119.12): disastrous.

to ribbons (119.16–17): very much.

to the bone (119.17): to the very limit; to the extreme.

goodwill (119.20): friendly disposition.

abyss (119.22): endless space; a very deep hole.

crevice (119.24): a narrow crack or opening.

precipice (119.25): a very steep side of a cliff.

calyx (119.28): the group of leaves which enclose and protect a flower bud.

foot (120.1): bottom; base.

void (120.5): large and empty.

milestone (120.21): a stone indicating the number of miles to a certain place.

Orientals (120.26): people from the East.

raison d'être (120.29): reason for existing.

reins of her own life (121.1–2): the control of her own life.

gulls (121.9): seabirds.

chafed (121.24): became irritated and impatient.

'THE FLYING FISH'

Focus
What do you think is meant by the 'Greater Day'?

Follow-up
What is significant about the flying fish?

Do you think that the story is mainly realistic or mainly symbolic?

What impression is given of Mexico? What words does D. H. Lawrence use to describe the country?

What difference is made between city/town and countryside?

How are Americans represented? Why do you think they are shown in this way?

cablegram (123.1): telegram.

malaria (123.7): a disease caused by the bite of certain mosquitoes.

parched (123.7): hot and dry.

lethargy (123.9): lack of energy and enthusiasm.

ennui (123.9): boredom and dissatisfaction because nothing interesting is thought to be happening.

pathos (123.10): a quality which causes a feeling of sadness and pity.

plateaux (123.12): large areas of fairly level ground high above the surrounding land.

tierra caliente (123.13): (Spanish) hot land or region.

flora (123.16): flowers and plants.

essences (123.18): extracts from plants.

toxins (123.18): poisonous substances.

the Mayas, the Zapotecas, and the Aztecs (123.19–20): native Mexican peoples. The Mayas flourished between AD 500 and 900. After the eleventh century, the Zapotecs, a nomadic tribe, settled in the mountains near Oaxaca. The Aztecs founded Mexico City in 1325, but were defeated by the Spanish explorer Cortés in the 1520s.

quinine (123.22): a bitter-tasting drug used in the treatment of malaria.

patio (124.2): paved courtyard.

Buena de Noche (124.3): (Spanish) the name for various plants that bloom at night and give off a heavy, fragrant perfume.

nada más (124.7): (Spanish) nothing more.

trefoil (124.17): any structure with three parts.

vellum (124.21): high-quality parchment made from the skins of calves, lambs or young goats.

Elizabethan (124.29): relating to the life and times of Elizabeth I, who reigned from 1558 to 1603.

uncanny (125.6): keen; precise; penetrating.

to come into your own (125.10–11): to gain your inheritance; in this context, to gain self-possession.

futility (125.14): pointlessness; ineffectiveness.

fair copy (125.17): a version of a document that has been written out again.

alluded to (125.24–5): referred to.

evening star (125.26): a bright planet seen in the western sky at sunset. It is usually Venus but, on occasions, Mercury.

unclipt (125.36): unclipped.

dilettante (126.5): typical of someone who has a superficial understanding of something.

highflown (126.5): having an unconvincing elegance and refinement; pretentious.

fissures (126.10): long, deep cracks.

stifle (126.28): suffocate.

tropics (127.3): places with a hot climate, usually in the area between the Tropic of Cancer and the Tropic of Capricorn.

calico (127.11): a type of cotton.

flitted (127.11): moved quickly.

transit (127.13): the process of going from one place to another.

Americano (127.22): an American or any English-speaking foreigner.

grille (127.23): criss-crossed bars.

pullulating (127.24): increasing rapidly.

por amor de Dios (127.25): (Spanish) for the love of God.

Mixtec (127.28): a native, nomadic, Mexican tribe who, like the Zapotecs, settled in the hills near Oaxaca in the eleventh century.

calomel (127.31): a medicine which clears out the system.

refrain (128.5): chorus.

hemmed in (128.6): enclosed.

plaza (128.10): an open square or marketplace.

canna (128.12): a tropical plant with clusters of red or yellow flowers.

baroque (128.18): highly ornate and decorative.

annulled (128.32): totally destroyed or wiped out.

permeates (128.34): enters and spreads throughout.

little revolutions (129.1–2): In 1923, Adolfo Huerta (1881–1955) rebelled against the government. He won great support from the army, but was defeated and driven into exile. Many small, local uprisings ('little revolutions') were linked to the national revolution.

narrow-gauge (129.4): a railway line whose tracks are less far apart than standard-gauge tracks.

barranca (129.5): (Spanish) a deep, narrow valley.

cleft (129.6): a gap between two things.

vital (129.18): alive.

petty (129.21): small; insignificant.

hearth (129.22): the floor of a fireplace, but symbolically representative of the home and family life.

sloe-bushes (129.30): bushes that bear dark purple, red or yellow fruits (sloes).

caravan (130.20): a group of travellers.

defile (130.21): a narrow mountain pass.

bulbous (131.3): rounded and swollen-looking.

los venados (131.7): (Spanish) the deer.

majolica tiles (131.21): highly decorated ceramic tiles coated with a tin oxide glaze.

hacienda (131.28): a large estate, ranch or farm.

Tlascala tribe (131.34): the Tlaxaltec Indians settled in Tlaxcala, east of Mexico City. They fought on the side of Cortés against the Aztecs in the sixteenth century.

Quiere helados, Señor? (131.35–6): (Spanish) would you like ice-cream, sir?

Gracias (132.2): (Spanish) thank you.

padrón (132.3): (Spanish) master.

centavos (132.4): coins of small value. The unit of currency in Mexico is the peso, and there are 100 centavos in a peso.

crooning (132.6): soft singing or murmuring.

marrow (132.9): the core, essence or key part.

Lasciate ogni speranza, voi ch'entrate (132.10): (Italian) Abandon all hope, you who enter. A quotation from Dante's *Inferno*. The words are inscribed over the gate of Hell.

Perdite ogni pianto, voi ch'uscite (132.11): (Italian) Lose all tears, you who depart.

the volcano of Orizaba (132.27): Pico de Orizaba is Mexico's highest volcano. It has been extinct for quite a long time.

cease (132.34): stop.

time-space continuum (133.7): In 1905, Einstein published his Special Theory of Relativity, which replaced the concept of space as independent of time with the idea of a four-dimensional space-time continuum consisting of three spatial coordinates and one for time, in which it is possible to locate events.

shroud (133.14): cover; wrap.

abide (133.25): stay; keep.

maketh (133.27): makes.

twinkleth (133.28): twinkles.

lieth (133.34): lies.

Vesuvius (133.34): an active volcano in Italy. It overlooks the Bay of Naples.

spitteth (133.34): spits.

Nemesis (133.36): deserved punishment; fate. In Greek myth, the avenger, a personification of the gods' revenge.

Erinyes . . . Furies (134.1): In Greek mythology, the Furies are female spirits who tormented wrongdoers, especially those who committed crimes against members of their own family.

knowest (134.3): know.

canst (134.5): can.

take heed (134.6): take notice; pay attention.

impiety (134.8): lack of respect.

equipage (134.12): a particularly fine horse-drawn carriage and its attendants.

Pullman car (134.12–13): a very comfortable railway carriage in which you can sit or sleep.

gardenias (134.21): fragrant white flowers.

Veracruz (134.23): (Spanish: True Cross) a city and port in Mexico, situated on the Gulf of Mexico.

customs buildings (134.25): buildings where people have to report when entering a country and where goods and baggage are examined to see if duty is payable.

pianofortes (134.25): a formal name for pianos.

commerce (134.26): trade; the buying and selling of goods.

socialists (134.33): people who believe in and support the view that a country's land, transport, natural resources and chief industries should be owned and controlled by everyone or by the state, and that wealth should be evenly and equally distributed.

jetty (135.2): a platform that is built out in the sea and to which boats can be tied.

steamer (135.3): a ship or boat that is powered by steam.

cargo boat (135.3): a boat that primarily carries goods rather than passengers.

primeval (135.4): belonging to the very earliest period of history; very ancient.

nullity (135.6): no value or importance; amounting to nothing.

nihilism (135.6): belief that nothing is worthwhile and everything is pointless.

affairs (135.10): business.

saloon (135.12): a large public room on board a ship where people can sit and relax.

compulsion (135.16): the state of being made, or forced, to do something, usually against the will.

mealy-mouthed (135.18): unwilling to speak openly and plainly.

Mammon (135.18): wealth and riches in the sense of their being a bad influence.

bulwark (135.22): protection; safeguard.

merchants (135.26): people who buy and sell goods.

fêted (135.28): lavishly entertained.

knight (136.2): in the UK, a person who has been given an honorary rank for services to the country and who is addressed by the title 'Sir'.

flanked by (136.8): having on either side.

buffer-state (136.10): a neutral area between two opposing, hostile states.

stewards (136.12): people who attend the passengers on a ship.

lorgnette (136.18): spectacles with a long handle at the side.

countenance (136.19): in a state of being controlled and composed. The phrase 'out of countenance' suggesting the opposite is used here ironically.

bluff (136.21): friendly but tactlessly outspoken and not taking into account the feelings of others.

brayed (136.23): spoke in a loud voice.

Galician Spanish (136.23): Galicia is an isolated province in north-western Spain. Galicians speak a dialect that is half Spanish and half Portuguese.

wine-decanter (136.32): a decorative bottle used for storing and serving wine.

ad lib. (136.34): (Latin) in this context, freely, liberally and without restraint.

à discrétion (136.34): (French) with discretion, with restraint and prudence; under control.

got a shot at it (136.36–137.1): had a go at it.

Basque (137.5): a person who comes from a specific area in northern Spain.

wants (137.7): needs.

gangway (137.13): a narrow passage-way.

liner (137.18): a passenger ship.

bowsprit (137.21): a pole that projects forward from the front of a ship.

candid (137.23): direct; honest; refreshing; forthright.

pinion-spray (137.25): spray in the form of wings at each side.

grasshoppers (138.14): insects that jump high and make a short, high-pitched sound.

locusts (138.14): insects that fly in large groups and destroy crops.

snouts (138.33): the noses and mouths of animals.

abashed (138.34): embarrassed; ashamed.

pristine (139.4): clear and clean.

porpoises (139.5): marine mammals related to dolphins and whales.

torpedo (139.14): a cylindrical underwater weapon that travels at considerable speed.

tail-flukes (139.18): the horizontal parts of the tail which are used to propel the animal through the water.

owls (140.22): stupid and clumsy people.

port-hole (141.2): a round window in the side of a ship.

Havana (141.3): port, capital and largest city of Cuba.

wharf (141.5): a landing-place for ships.

boulevard (141.5): a wide, tree-lined street.

mass (141.7): a religious ceremony (Communion) in the Roman Catholic and some Protestant Churches.

colloquial (141.14): informal.

oil-fields of Tampico (141.15): the oil-fields of Tampico on the Gulf of Mexico were discovered and developed from 1901 to 1921, mainly with foreign money and expertise.

chauffeur (141.16): a person employed to drive a car.

Yankees (141.16): a slang term for people from the United States of America.

Red Cross work (141.27): the Red Cross is an international organization which cares for the sick and wounded in wars and natural disasters. The term is used ironically here.

muy bien (141.30): (Spanish) very good.

acrid (141.32): bitter.

villas (142.5): small houses in a residential area.

spick-and-span (142.6): clean, neat and tidy.

Connecticut . . . New Jersey . . . Louisiana . . . Georgia (142.12): States in the United States of America.

Conquistadores. . . Columbus (142.16): this refers to the Spanish who originally conquered the Americas, beginning with Christopher Columbus's discovery in 1492.

hock (142.19): a white wine from Germany.

Burgundy (142.19): a red or white wine produced in France.

reel (142.21): spin.

esplanade (142.22): a long, level road or walkway, especially at the side of the sea.

fort (142.29): a building or buildings that have been especially made for the military defence of an area.

See Naples and die (142.34): an obscure Italian proverb which suggests that after seeing Naples there is nothing more beautiful left on earth to see.

sombre (143.4): dark, dull and gloomy.

latitude (143.12): the distance of a place north or south of the Equator, measured in degrees.

lost world of Atlantis (143.17): a fabled, powerful island kingdom in the Atlantic Ocean that was supposed to have sunk under the sea.

swell (143.20): the rising and falling of a large area of the sea as a long wave travels through without breaking; in this context, rough sea is suggested.

entrails (143.32): internal organs.

plague-ship (143.34): ship hulks that were moored away from the shore were used by the British to isolate people who were suffering from infectious diseases.

chirruping (144.10): making short, sharp sounds like those made by birds.

Sauerkraut (144.18): cabbage cut up into small pieces and pickled.

Further Activities and Study Questions

FURTHER ACTIVITIES

'Her Turn'
The narrator does not seem to side with either of the characters. Re-write the story briefly from: (a) the woman's point of view; (b) the man's point of view.

'Odour of Chrysanthemums'

Walter Bates is never present, alive, in the story. Imagine that you are him and present his version of his life and death in about 500 words.

'You Touched Me'

Write a short (two or three paragraphs) piece in which you imagine what will happen to the characters after the end of the story.

The Fox

Imagine that you are Banford and write down your impressions of Henry: (a) when he first arrives at the farm; (b) when he tells Banford that March is going to marry him.

'The Flying Fish'

This was unfinished; briefly continue the story in your own words. Give a brief outline of what you think happens to Gethin Day when he gets back to England.

STUDY QUESTIONS

Discuss the presentation of women in the stories. How does Lawrence present women? Are they presented the same in all the stories? Are women presented in a positive fashion? Does Lawrence show them as strong or weak characters?

In 'Odour of Chrysanthemums', what impression is given of working-class life and the environment? How does it differ from that presented in 'Her Turn'? Would you say that one presents a better picture than the other? If so, in what ways?

How does Lawrence address issues of social class in the stories? Are these issues evident in all the stories or just some of them? Think about such things as the way Lawrence portrays the working classes and the way he portrays the middle classes.

Choose two stories that seem to share similar themes and discuss Lawrence's presentation of these themes. For instance, 'Her Turn' and 'Odour of Chrysanthemums' both seem to be about the families of coal-miners, while 'You Touched Me' and *The Fox* both appear to be types of love story.

Choose three stories and compare the endings. Discuss whether the endings are satisfactory. Do the stories end too quickly? Are the endings conclusive? Do they seem to finish off the story properly or are you left wondering what will happen?

Character Notes

'HER TURN'

Mrs Radford

She is an intelligent woman who thoroughly understands her husband and knows how to handle him, even if she has to do this in a crafty way. She seems to be more clever than her husband. She appears to be happily married on the whole. She is thrifty and saves her money. Her husband's reaction to her victory does frighten her and she shows disappointment that he had almost to resort to violence.

Mr Radford

He is a genial, likeable man, someone who enjoys spending money on himself and drinking in public houses. He is probably not quite as clever as he thinks he is and, although his wife might not have sufficient physical strength to defeat him, she certainly has more cunning. Despite his likeable nature, he could resort to violence, although this time he restrains himself.

'ODOUR OF CHRYSANTHEMUMS'

Elizabeth Bates

She is the principal character in the story. She is a proud, strong woman and is rather neglected by her husband, who spends much of his free time drinking at the public house. At first, we tend to sympathize with her and see her husband as a not very likeable character. However, when her husband is killed, we see a different side to the story and to her character. Elizabeth has to admit that her husband has been almost a stranger to her and that she has never understood him. His death forces her to see that there have been faults on both sides, and she feels both regretful and humbled.

'YOU TOUCHED ME'

Hadrian

He is a member of the lower classes who is eager to take opportunities and is keen to achieve a better position in society. He has been adopted into the Rockley family but never felt a proper part of it when he was younger, as he was not able to conform to their standards and was patronized by the sisters. On his return, he seems to show genuine affection towards Mr Rockley. Hadrian is a complex character. He is interested in power as well as money. He is to some extent crafty and cunning, but he is also brave and resourceful.

Matilda

She is the elder of the two sisters. She is more interested in artistic and intellectual pursuits than in housekeeping. She is concerned with her appearance and how she looks to Hadrian. She is rather proud, haughty and conscious of her position in society, but she is not as much of a snob or so lacking in respect for Hadrian as is her younger sister. She is very emotional and is devoted to her father, as is evidenced by her seeming to be in a dazed state when she realizes the extent of his illness.

Emmie

Emmie is more down-to-earth and practical than Matilda. Her life revolves around taking care of the house. However, she is also more aware of, and concerned about, her social position. She is very jealous of Hadrian and of his influence over her father. She displays a dislike of the lower classes and is very sarcastic and angry. She appears to possess very few positive features and her dominant emotions are anger, contempt and jealousy.

Mr Rockley

He is a man who considers that having a son is important, which is why he originally adopts Hadrian and why he is eager for Hadrian to marry Matilda. He is obviously someone who is used to getting his own way and he is quite ruthless, especially where the feelings of his daughters are concerned. He is the only person who is truly satisfied with the marriage of Matilda and Hadrian.

THE FOX

March

March is a contradictory character. She is very practical, unafraid of hard, manual labour, yet at the same time she is someone who is very vague, often lost in thought. She experiences trance-like states and is subject to strange thoughts and feelings. She is highly emotional, affected by the fox and its powerful presence to the extent that she seems dazed and confused. She seems unsatisfied with the farm, but does not appear to know what she wants. Yet she is physically, and in some ways mentally, strong; a forceful woman who is used to taking control of her life. At the same time powerful natural forces – the fox and Henry – appear to overcome her, but she fights and strives against total domination.

Banford

Banford is another contradictory character. She is not an evil villain, despite the fact that she is destined to die. She is shown at her best when she first entertains Henry, acting in a loving, sisterly way. Nevertheless, she does have some unattractive qualities: she is nervous, frail, clinging to March, enveloping her with a parasitic, sterile love. She is jealous and devious, prepared to use all her powers of persuasion to prevent the marriage of March and Henry.

Henry Grenfel

Henry is also a complex character, probably the most complex in the story. He is not altogether attractive, and it is significant that he is associated with the fox, an animal that inspires contradictory emotions because it is seen as powerful, virile, a symbol of masculinity, but also a crafty and cunning predator. On the positive side, he is energetic, youthful, determined and skilled. He appears as a revitalizing force. However, he is also ruthless, determined at all costs to have his way. He is a hunter who hunts and kills his prey in a cold and calculating manner. It is difficult to explain away his actions and be totally sympathetic towards him after he has killed Banford.

'THE FLYING FISH'

Gethin Day

It is difficult to comment on Gethin Day's character and how it would have developed if Lawrence had finished the story. From the fragment that we have, Day appears world-weary and ill. He seems to be hemmed in by the lesser day, the ordinary, humdrum life, but is always searching for something better, the Greater Day. He is revitalized and brought to a new awareness by the 'flying fish' and can be seen as an example of Lawrence's regenerate man.

Text Summaries

'HER TURN'

Mr and Mrs Radford are reasonably happily married. Mrs Radford is Mr Radford's second wife. He is friendly, genial, but quite naïve, although he thinks of himself as clever; a keen solver of conundrums. She is intelligent and cunning. The family have sufficient money to live comfortably. Radford gives his wife thirty-five shillings a week when he is working, but some time ago, when on strike, he did not give her any of his strike-pay. When a second strike occurs, she prepares a plan. One night she asks for some of the strike-pay, but she is told that she has plenty of her own money that she must use. The next day, she buys various items for the house with her savings. When the articles that she has bought are delivered, Radford is perplexed and astonished, but he cannot claim that they are not needed. He is even asked to tip the delivery man as Mrs Radford has no change. After the delivery has been made, she shows her husband that she has very little money left. He becomes angry and it seems that he is going to hit her, but he turns away and goes into the garden. The next week, Radford hands over his strike-pay to his wife and she gives him back a small amount for himself.

'ODOUR OF CHRYSANTHEMUMS'

Elizabeth Bates, a coal miner's wife, is waiting for her husband, Walter, to return home from work. She thinks that he has gone to the public house and will come home drunk, as he usually does.

She prepares a meal which she shares with her two children. Still her husband does not return. She puts the children to bed and becomes increasingly worried. She goes out to call on a neighbour, Mrs Rigley, to enquire if Mr Rigley has returned. Jack Rigley has returned home, had his dinner and gone out again. Mrs Rigley fetches her husband, who offers to go and see if he can find Walter. He cannot remember seeing Walter leave the coal mine. Elizabeth returns home. Some time later her mother-in-law arrives and appears upset. She tells Elizabeth that Jack Rigley has visited her to inform her that her son has had an accident. Elizabeth, who is pregnant, worries what will happen to herself and her family if her husband is injured. A miner arrives to tell them that Walter has been killed in an accident in the mine. The body is brought home and placed in the parlour. The two women wash the body and prepare it for burial. While they are doing this, Elizabeth thinks about her husband and their life together and she realizes that she never really knew or understood him. She sees that there were faults on both sides in the marriage.

'YOU TOUCHED ME'

The story is set just after the end of the First World War. Matilda and Emmie, two sisters, live with their father, who is ill, in Pottery House. The women have not married because there has been a lack of suitable prospective husbands in the appropriate social class. Some years before, Ted Rockley, the women's father, had adopted an orphan boy named Hadrian. The family, while not totally resenting the boy, did restrict him and try to make him conform to their standards. He did not altogether fit in with the family and, when he reached fifteen, Hadrian decided to leave England for Canada. During the war, he had joined the army and had fought in Europe. Now that the war is over, he is returning to Pottery House for a visit. He arrives earlier than expected while the sisters are still cleaning the house. Emmie is not pleased with his arrival, but Mr Rockley is happy to see him. One night, Mr

Rockley tells Matilda that he wants Hadrian to have his watch and chain and one hundred pounds after his death. Matilda is very upset and becomes preoccupied with thoughts of her father dying. It is as if she is in a trance. That night, still in a trance-like state, she enters what she thinks is her father's bedroom. She touches the figure in the bed, who awakes. It is Hadrian and she has entered his bedroom by mistake. The next day, Hadrian tells Mr Rockley that he will marry Matilda if he wants him to, and he asks Mr Rockley to ask her on his behalf. After two days, Mr Rockley approaches his daughter, who is shocked and astounded. She resists the offer, and Mr Rockley threatens to change his will and give all his money to Hadrian if she does not change her mind. Eventually she agrees and the couple are married. Both are uncertain of the future and only Mr Rockley seems entirely satisfied with the marriage.

THE FOX

March and Banford, two unmarried women, run a small farm together. They are from the city and are inexperienced, so the farm does not prosper. The only livestock they have is ducks and chickens, and these are stolen regularly by a fox. March decides to keep watch and encounters the fox. She seems transfixed by the animal and is unable to shoot it.

Months pass, and one evening in November the women are visited by Henry Grenfel. He is a young soldier who has been fighting in the First World War, which has just ended. Originally from Cornwall, he had emigrated to Canada some time before. Now that he is back in England, he was intending to visit his grandfather, who had once owned the farm. He did not know that his grandfather had died. The women invite him in and offer him some food. He reminds March of the fox, but Banford is pleased to entertain him. They offer him a room, since they think it unlikely that he will find accommodation in the village. The next day it is decided that he can stay on for a while and help with the farm work. A day or two later, Henry suddenly decides that he would like to marry March, and one night he asks her. She cannot give him an answer, but later, after Banford has gone to bed, Henry asks her again and she accepts. The next morning, Henry tells Banford, who is upset, angry and jealous. That night Banford tries to persuade March not to marry him. Henry overhears her. Then he goes out and hunts and kills the fox. The same night, March has a dream that Banford is dead and that she has to cover her with the fox skin. Henry tells Banford that after he and March are married they will leave for Canada. Banford is very upset and again tries to persuade March to change her mind about the marriage. Henry has to leave to return to the army, but the wedding is eventually fixed for Christmas, when he will return.

Nine days later, he receives a letter from March saying that the marriage was a foolish idea and she no longer wishes to marry him. Henry is angry, so he obtains leave from his captain and sets off to bicycle to the farm.

At the farm, Banford's parents are visiting. Banford, her father and March are looking at a tree that March has been trying to cut down. Henry arrives and offers to help. He takes the axe and tells Banford to move because, if she does not, the falling tree may hit her. Henry secretly hopes that she will not move as he wants her to die. Banford is stubborn and refuses to move, and when the tree falls it hits and kills her. March marries Henry as originally planned and they go to Cornwall, his home county. The story ends with the two of them sitting and looking out to sea, contemplating their future lives.

'THE FLYING FISH'

The story opens in Mexico, as Gethin Day is recovering from a serious illness which has nearly killed him. He receives a telegram with the message that he must return to his family home, Daybrook, immediately. The house has been in his family for many, many years and it is thought that there will be bad luck if there is no Day living at Daybrook.

Text Summaries

One of Gethin's ancestors, Sir Gilbert Day, had written a book that was felt to be important in the family. Gethin knows much of it by heart, especially that part concerned with the 'Greater Day', for which he seems to be searching.

Gethin catches a train which takes him to the port of Veracruz, where he embarks on a ship for his voyage home. During the voyage, day after day Gethin watches porpoises and dolphins and he is almost spellbound by their beauty and agility. He comes to the conclusion that they are able to achieve pure joy and he feels that they are able to teach mankind a lesson about togetherness. In some sense, these 'flying fish' represent the 'Greater Day'.

The ship docks at Havana, Cuba. Gethin tours around, but finds it depressing. The ships leaves, and next morning they are travelling in the dull, grey Atlantic. The ship enters rough seas and the story, which is unfinished, ends as the weather becomes calm again.

Critical Responses

'Her Turn', though originally rejected by the *Daily News* and the journal *Eyewitness,* was first published in the *Westminster Gazette* in September 1913. It was reprinted in English and American magazines in the summer of 1934, and later in the same year appeared in the collection *A Modern Lover.* There seems to be no early critical comment on the story, and *A Modern Lover* appears to have found little favour with the critics. Currie Cabot, writing in the *Saturday Review of Literature*, claims that 'there is no story in the collection that touches Lawrence at his absolute best',[1] while Dilys Powell in the *London Mercury* comments that the book was only 'second rate'.[2]

Later critics have remarked upon the story, but not at any great length. E. W. Tedlock Jr, in *D. H. Lawrence: Artist and Rebel,* sees it as a comic treatment of 'the contest between . . . men and the "conscience keepers" who thwart them', commenting that 'the story turns on his [the man's] wife's dissatisfaction when, during a strike, she cannot get his strike-pay from him, and the stratagem she uses during the next strike'.[3] Tedlock sees the woman in a positive light, describing her as 'not a puritanical shrew, but a clever combiner of the main chance with passional claim'.[4] Philip Hobsbaum states that the story is 'handled in a lighter vein',[5] but skilfully nevertheless. He views the story as highlighting the wife's attempt to assert 'her personality in the marriage' and succeeding 'in her endeavour'.[6] Remarking on 'Her Turn' and Lawrence's other stories about miners, including 'Odour of Chrysanthemums', Hobsbaum concludes that '[they] impress me as being as good as anything Lawrence did in a naturalistic vein. They grow out of the very bones of his Englishness.'[7]

Janice Hubbard Harris, in *The Short Fiction of D. H. Lawrence*, contends that 'Her Turn', like the other strike sketches, avoids sentimentality by the specificity of its details and by the complexity of the human relationships it manages to convey.'[8] She sees the story as a 'glimpse into these people's lives', one that is 'brief but rich in insight and detail'.[9]

After initially appearing in the *English Review*, 'Odour of Chrys-anthemums' was included in *The Prussian Officer and Other Stories*, published in November 1914. Critics reviewing this volume were not overly impressed with the stories, remarking on their morbid and unpleasant nature. However, the reviewer for the *Glasgow Herald* adopted a more positive attitude, describing them as 'sincere in truthful passion and taut with painful life'.[10] Similarly, the reviewer in *Outlook* described the stories as 'all brilliant, all super-human, and at the same time *in*human',[11] concluding rather doubt-fully: 'We do not think it would ever be possible for Mr Lawrence to conceive characters whose blood courses at a normal rate or whose passions are not Gargantuan. But if he should ever be minded to describe them in their tired, or rather their exhausted, moods we should perhaps find their humanity.'[12]

Reviews were not actually poor, but most made the point that, while the stories were powerful, they were also depressing and brutal. We have to remember that the book was published during the First World War, and undoubtedly the critics' attitude was in part coloured by this, with the accompanying perceived need for fiction to present an optimistic outlook.

Later critics, focusing on 'Odour of Chrysanthemums' itself, have been more understanding. Graham Hough calls the story 'admirable', commenting:

Depth and complexity are added in the final scene by showing it through the eyes of two women, his wife and mother, with radically different attitudes. If we do not require Lawrence's peculiar insight, its possibilities and all its perils, these stories are as perfect achievements, on their own scale, as anything he wrote.[13]

E. W. Tedlock Jr claims that through the story 'runs the extreme failure in relationship which is the Lawrencean tragedy'.[14] He continues:

Much more should be said of this story than that it is characteristically Lawrencean in perception and theme. It is an example of his art at its organic best. Tone, setting, dialogue and action, a pervasively suggestive imagery of deathliness through ragged garden, autumn, and odor of chrys-anthemums, all create a felt meaning of cumulative fatality now being climactically realized.[15]

Keith Sagar also takes a positive view of the story, seeing it as 'the first sign of the mature style, apparently sparse and restrained, yet able to draw on real poetic resources, and applied to the human predicament within the domestic and mining scene'.[16] Summing up, he comments that 'men and women, at the mercy of the machine, breathe an atmosphere of death, heightened by the odour of chrysanthemums'.[17]

In *A Reader's Guide to D. H. Lawrence*, Hobsbaum is similarly approving, describing the story as 'a work of art'.[18] He goes on to discuss the image of the chrysanthemums, but concludes:

At this point the chrysanthemums recede in significance. They were there to symbolize the better qualities of the poor wretch, in life as well as death. His old mother says that he was a happy lad when he was young. This makes one feel that he grew up to be an unhappy man. His body in death is beautiful – ' "clear and clean and white" ', murmurs the old mother. The wife recognizes, however, that in life she had rejected him as a body and as a person.[19]

Gāmini Salgādo considers that, when the miner's body is brought home, 'the narrative takes on a more ritualistic and elegiac qual-ity',[20] and claims that 'By a profound but familiar paradox, the intimate acquaintance with death, though unnerving, becomes a means to a richer recognition of life's possibilities, however meagre.'[21]

'You Touched Me' was published in 1922 in the collection of stories entitled *England, My England*. In an unsigned review in the

New York Times Book Review, 'You Touched Me' was described as 'a very peculiar story',[22] while the reviewer, commenting on the collection as a whole, remarked: 'All this is of the simplest, the most easily understood; but beneath, like the blood and muscles and nerves beneath the skin, is a whole throbbing, sensitive organism of desires and motives and emotions of which even their possessors are often unaware.'[23]

In the *Times Literary Supplement*, A. S. McDowell specifically remarks on 'You Touched Me' and another story, 'Samson and Delilah', praising them for their vividness and beauty, but finding that 'these stories are certainly not "pleasant" and their author has a way of closing the escapes for us'.[24]

F. R. Leavis claims that 'You Touched Me' could 'hardly be called a love story'.[25] He sees Hadrian as a regenerative figure: 'Hadrian stands for life, and the marriage is the assurance of a living future; we know, without needing to be told in so many words, that essentially the dying man sees the dead-end of old-maidhood in the Pottery House as a defeat of life.'[26]

Touching on 'You Touched Me' in connection with other stories, Graham Hough seems somewhat less approving when he puts forward the view that: 'Relations between men and women are always relations of conflict, and lovers rarely seem ever to have any ordinary human understanding of each other: all the stress is on bonds other than conscious ones.'[27] Hough remarks that 'a claim, a bond or an attractive force exerts itself in flat opposition to the normal sentimental disposition of the characters', and continues: 'People are always being driven to do just what they do not want to do – women marry the men they hate without apparently modifying their hatred; men marry women who are certain to make them unhappy. Lawrence feels the primacy of unconsciousness and unrecognized forces so strongly that he must show them harshly victorious.'[28]

Tedlock sees the story as dealing with issues of class, developing 'the theme of the active raid on the middle-class world by the lower-class man',[29] and concludes that 'this Lawrencean variation on the old middle-class moral theme of the mercenary struggle over an inheritance, has something of the pattern but none of the rich symbolism of "The Fox".'[30]

Hubbard Harris also links the story to *The Fox*, seeing both as presenting us with 'sadly broken females, no longer young, desperately in need of rescue'.[31] The male character in both tales is described as 'crude, young, dangerous, calculating, vibrant; he is very much the returning stranger'.[32] Hubbard Harris finds 'You Touched Me' problematic, considering that it probably works best as a fable, acting out 'the myth of the revivifying stranger; as a metaphor for the necessary fertilization of the genteel classes by the lower'.[33] Reading it this way, she thinks, it is just about palatable, but she continues that 'the problem is the tale cannot be read as only fable'.[34] She sums up:

Most important, in 'The Fox', 'You Touched Me', and many of the tales to follow, one sees Lawrence dramatizing the notion encoded through centuries of law and custom that there is real gain for man and woman alike in the woman's giving up self-responsibility. The gain derives of course from the fact that each is following his and her 'natural' bent, his to lead, hers to follow.[35]

The Fox, a considerably longer work, was initially published in an American magazine, *The Dial*, and then in book form with *The Ladybird* and *The Captain's Doll* in 1923.

Early critical reception appears, on the whole, favourable. In an unsigned review in *The Times Literary Supplement*, the female characters are described as 'intensely real, closely and humorously studied'.[36] The reviewer goes on to remark that 'there is a touch of fantasy in the fox's spell, which merges, however, in a sense of oneness between man and nature',[37] and concludes: 'The atmosphere around the farm is drawn close with a physical tenseness – the attraction is inexplicable, painful, almost terrible and brings a tragedy; yet it is possible, and we feel that Mr Lawrence is in control of it.'[38]

Charles Marriott in the *Manchester Guardian* comments: 'His constant theme is the perplexing nature of love as an expression of life. That, as in *The Fox*, love should lead to crime does not for a moment identify it with lust.'[39] Marriott is impressed by the volume as a whole, remarking that 'it is doubtful if anything in recent fiction combines so true an impression of life with so vivid an account of the accidents of living'.[40]

An unsigned review appeared in *The Spectator* where the reviewer, discussing *The Fox*, considers that 'the story is very strange; it moves, as does real life or as does the best sort of lyrical poetry, upon two or three planes of consciousness at once, the result is an extreme richness of texture'.[41]

Moving to later critics, Leavis feels that *The Fox*'s 'strength lies – and it is one of the supreme things among the major tales – in the fulness, depth, and unambiguous clarity with which it presents its theme'.[42] For Leavis, it is a drama with 'emotional depth and dignity'[43] and 'fully and unequivocally a study of love'.[44] However, he does not see it as an ordinary love story, but 'a study of human mating; of the attraction between a man and a woman that expresses the profound needs of each and has its meaning in a permanent union'.[45] Leavis has no problems with Banford's death, stating that 'the willed accident is the external event that completes the significance of the essential Laurentian drama – Henry *had* to will Banford's death'.[46]

Hough sees *The Fox* as 'one of Lawrence's masterpieces of straightforward naturalistic narrative'.[47] He claims that it is possible to see the female characters as Lawrencean types, with the 'frail affectionate, spectacled Banford as a representative of "white" passionless love, and the ruddy, physically effective March as natural energy unawakened or misdirected'.[48] Commenting on the ending, Hough seemingly equates the life of an animal with that of a human being, but when speculating on the ending, he does implicitly question Lawrence's solutions:

Then he sees that it was not enough to kill the fox, he must also kill Banford. And when he has done so we reach one of those typical endings which is no ending; there is no future for him and March in their present surroundings, they must go out for Canada – they must pass on, that is to say, to somewhere outside the confines of the story altogether. The characteristic solution for Lawrence – to move on and start again some-where else.[49]

Monroe Engel remarks on the 'markedly objective style verging on irony, or a kind of satire with only the mutest comedy'.[50] However, he comments that the story suffers from 'a kind of heaviness from which the subsequent short novels do not suffer'.[51] He also complains about the weakness of the final pages 'which attempt to get at what the nature of the new kind of relationship between man and woman will be'.[52]

Tedlock sees the story as reflecting 'Lawrence's surrealistic sense of psychic disorder in the wartime world'.[53] Banford's murder, rather than being questioned, is described as 'a struggle for survival in which the murder is vitalistically ethical'.[54] Moreover, Tedlock considers the unresolved ending a strength, 'for the Lawrencean conflict could never be fully resolved as long as the old values persisted, as long as Lawrence did not oversimplify, and as long as he was self-critical'.[55]

On the other hand, Sagar, although describing *The Fox* as impressive, views the case of Banford as 'altogether more complex' and feels that she is 'never established as a merely deadly, life-consuming creature'.[56] Sagar contends that 'Lawrence makes no attempt to humanise in Henry the qualities of the fox',[57] and furthermore '[He] uses the man/fox identification to evade res-ponsibilities for human consciousness, and to render the taking of human life in terms morally equivalent to the fox's taking of a hen. Henry is shown responding to moral imperatives from within himself which tell him that Banford is deadly (i.e. opposed to his own purposes) and must be killed.'[58]

Hobsbaum claims that it is on the whole a 'precisely told story', that falters after the death of Banford and 'modulates into a tone more lyrical and less actual', before coming to 'a rather uncertain halt'.[59]

'The Flying Fish' was not published until after Lawrence's death, when it appeared in *Phoenix: The Unpublished Papers of D. H. Lawrence*, in 1936. First reviewers were complimentary, with H. T.

Moore describing the fragment as 'one of the most important keys to Lawrence and one of the finest things he ever wrote'.[60] The reviewer in the *Observer* claimed that the flying fish passage 'surely stands among the finest pieces of descriptive writing'.[61] The *Criterion* review was similarly enthusiastic, referring to the 'outstanding loveliness'[62] of the passage, while Edward Garnett in the *London Mercury* called it 'one of the most beautiful things Lawrence wrote . . . a prose poem revealing Lawrence's genius in its purest essence'.[63]

Considering the descriptive 'flying fish' passages, a later critic, Keith Sagar, notes that 'Lawrence records their movements in limpid, delicate, sensitive prose'.[64] He continues:

Time and again the sentence seems to exhaust itself, only to recover with a new surge, each new clause suddenly appearing from nowhere to take up the meaning, to sustain the even onrush and gliding . . . the warm-bodied porpoises combine in perfect balance the instinctive life of the fish and the consciousness of the higher intelligence, the coldness of isolated pride and power . . . and the warmth of contact, love, laughter, interchange. Lawrence is seeking now some equivalent poise, harmony, first in an individual man, later in a society, a civilisation.[65]

Sagar concludes by remarking on the 'incredible beauty and serenity'[66] of 'The Flying Fish'.

Hubbard Harris links it to another story, 'The Escaped Cock', and puts forward the view that 'in general, they express the idea that there is a way of living and relating to others that escapes entanglements, compulsion, fret, conflict'.[67]

Overall, Lawrence's stories contained in this volume have received a varying amount of critical attention, most of it favourable, despite some questions being raised about certain aspects of *The Fox*.

NOTES

1. Currie Cabot, *Saturday Review of Literature*, xi, 273, 10 November 1934.

2. Dilys Powell, *London Mercury*, xxxi, 397, February 1935.

3. E. W. Tedlock Jr, *D. H. Lawrence: Artist and Rebel*, Albuquerque, University of New Mexico Press, 1963, p. 28.

4. Ibid., p. 29.

5. Philip Hobsbaum, *A Reader's Guide to D. H. Lawrence*, London, Thames and Hudson, 1981, p. 29.

6. Ibid.

7. Ibid., p. 31.

8. Janice Hubbard Harris, *The Short Fiction of D. H. Lawrence*, New Brunswick, New Jersey, Rutgers University Press, 1984, p. 65.

9. Ibid.

10. *Glasgow Herald*, 17 December 1914.

11. *Outlook*, 19 December 1914, xxxiv, 795–6.

12. Ibid.

13. Graham Hough, *The Dark Sun: A Study of D. H. Lawrence*, London, Duckworth, 1956, p. 170.

14. Tedlock, *D. H. Lawrence: Artist and Rebel*, p. 26.

15. Ibid.

16. Keith Sagar, *The Art of D. H. Lawrence*, Cambridge, Cambridge University Press, 1966, p. 14.

17. Ibid., p. 15.

18. Hobsbaum, *A Reader's Guide to D. H. Lawrence*, p. 27.

19. Ibid.

20. Gāmini Salgādo, *A Preface to Lawrence*, London, Longman, 1982, pp. 128–9.

21. Ibid., p. 129.

22. *New York Times Book Review*, 19 November 1922, pp. 13–14.

23. Ibid.

24. *The Times Literary Supplement*, 24 January 1924, p. 50.

25. F. R. Leavis, *D. H. Lawrence: Novelist*, London, Penguin, 1994 (first published 1955 by Chatto & Windus), p. 304.

26. Ibid., pp. 307–8.

27. Hough, *The Dark Sun: A Study of D. H. Lawrence*, p. 173.

28. Ibid., p. 174.

29. Tedlock, *D. H. Lawrence: Artist and Rebel*, p. 113.

30. Ibid., p. 114.

31. Hubbard Harris, *The Short Fiction of D. H. Lawrence*, p. 150.

32. Ibid., p. 151.

33. Ibid., p. 152.

34. Ibid.

35. Ibid., p. 153.

36. *The Times Literary Supplement*, 22 March 1923.

37. Ibid.

38. Ibid.

39. *Manchester Guardian*, 6 April 1923.

40. Ibid.

41. *Spectator*, 14 April 1923.

42. Leavis, *D. H. Lawrence: Novelist*, p. 309.

43. Ibid., p. 313.

44. Ibid., p. 314.

45. Ibid.

46. Ibid., p. 318.

47. Hough, *The Dark Sun: A Study of D. H. Lawrence*, p. 176.

48. Ibid.

49. Ibid., p. 177.

50. Monroe Engel, 'The Continuity of Lawrence's Short Novels', in *D. H. Lawrence: A Collection of Critical Essays*, ed. Mark Spilka, Eaglewood Cliffs, New Jersey, Prentice-Hall Inc., p. 93.

51. Ibid.

52. Ibid., p. 95.

53. Tedlock, *D. H. Lawrence: Artist and Rebel*, p. 116.

54. Ibid., p. 119.

55. Ibid.

56. Sagar, *The Art of D. H. Lawrence*, p. 116.

57. Ibid., p. 117.

58. Ibid.

59. Hobsbaum, *A Reader's Guide to D. H. Lawrence*, p. 107.

60. H. T. Moore, *Nation*, 24 October 1936.

61. *Observer*, 13 December 1936.
62. *Criterion*, July 1937.
63. Edward Garnett, *London Mercury*, December 1936.
64. Sagar, *The Art of D. H. Lawrence*, p. 208.
65. Ibid., pp. 208, 209–10.
66. Ibid., p. 210.
67. Hubbard Harris, *The Short Fiction of D. H. Lawrence*, p. 240.

Suggestions for Further Reading

Hobsbaum, Philip, *A Reader's Guide to D. H. Lawrence*, London, Thames and Hudson, 1981.

Hough, Graham, *The Dark Sun: A Study of D. H. Lawrence*, London, Duckworth, 1956.

Hubbard Harris, Janice, *The Short Fiction of D. H. Lawrence*, New Brunswick, New Jersey, Rutgers University Press, 1984.

Leavis, F. R., *D. H. Lawrence: Novelist*, London, Penguin, 1994.

Sagar, Keith, *The Art of D. H. Lawrence*, Cambridge, Cambridge University Press, 1966.

Tedlock, E. W., Jr, *D. H. Lawrence: Artist and Rebel*, Albuquerque, University of New Mexico Press, 1963.

Audio Extracts 🎧

'Her Turn'
pp. 3.1–9.3

'Odour of Chrysanthemums'
pp. 27.24–31.4

The Fox
1. pp. 50.1–55.4
2. pp. 58.33–62.23
3. pp. 117.22–122.6

'The Flying Fish'
pp. 137.16–140.34

Total = approx. 72 minutes

PENGUIN (P) CLASSICS

www.penguinclassics.com

- *Details about every Penguin Classic*

- *Advanced information about forthcoming titles*

- *Hundreds of author biographies*

- *FREE resources including critical essays on the books and their historical background, reader's and teacher's guides.*

- *Links to other web resources for the Classics*

- *Discussion area*

- *Online review copy ordering for academics*

- *Competitions with prizes, and challenging Classics trivia quizzes*

PENGUIN CLASSICS ONLINE

READ MORE IN PENGUIN

In every corner of the world, on every subject under the sun, Penguin represents quality and variety – the very best in publishing today.

For complete information about books available from Penguin – including Puffins, Penguin Classics and Arkana – and how to order them, write to us at the appropriate address below. Please note that for copyright reasons the selection of books varies from country to country.

In the United Kingdom: Please write to *Dept. EP, Penguin Books Ltd, Bath Road, Harmondsworth, West Drayton, Middlesex UB7 ODA*

In the United States: Please write to *Consumer Sales, Penguin Putnam Inc., P.O. Box 12289 Dept. B, Newark, New Jersey 07101-5289*. VISA and MasterCard holders call 1-800-788-6262 to order Penguin titles

In Canada: Please write to *Penguin Books Canada Ltd, 10 Alcorn Avenue, Suite 300, Toronto, Ontario M4V 3B2*

In Australia: Please write to *Penguin Books Australia Ltd, P.O. Box 257, Ringwood, Victoria 3134*

In New Zealand: Please write to *Penguin Books (NZ) Ltd, Private Bag 102902, North Shore Mail Centre, Auckland 10*

In India: Please write to *Penguin Books India Pvt Ltd, 11 Community Centre, Panchsheel Park, New Delhi 110017*

In the Netherlands: Please write to *Penguin Books Netherlands bv, Postbus 3507, NL-1001 AH Amsterdam*

In Germany: Please write to *Penguin Books Deutschland GmbH, Metzlerstrasse 26, 60594 Frankfurt am Main*

In Spain: Please write to *Penguin Books S. A., Bravo Murillo 19, 1° B, 28015 Madrid*

In Italy: Please write to *Penguin Italia s.r.l., Via Benedetto Croce 2, 20094 Corsico, Milano*

In France: Please write to *Penguin France, Le Carré Wilson, 62 rue Benjamin Baillaud, 31500 Toulouse*

In Japan: Please write to *Penguin Books Japan Ltd, Kaneko Building, 2-3-25 Koraku, Bunkyo-Ku, Tokyo 112*

In South Africa: Please write to *Penguin Books South Africa (Pty) Ltd, Private Bag X14, Parkview, 2122 Johannesburg*

READ MORE IN PENGUIN

Published or forthcoming:

Ulysses James Joyce

Written over a seven-year period, from 1914 to 1921, *Ulysses* has survived bowdlerization, legal action and bitter controversy. An undisputed modernist classic, its ceaseless verbal inventiveness and astonishingly wide-ranging allusions confirm its standing as an imperishable monument to the human condition. 'Everybody knows now that *Ulysses* is the greatest novel of the century' Anthony Burgess, *Observer*

Nineteen Eighty-Four George Orwell

Hidden away in the Record Department of the Ministry of Truth, Winston Smith skilfully rewrites the past to suit the needs of the Party. Yet he inwardly rebels against the totalitarian world he lives in, which controls him through the all-seeing eye of Big Brother. 'His final masterpiece . . . *Nineteen Eighty-Four* is enthralling' Timothy Garton Ash, *New York Review of Books*

The Day of the Locust *and* The Dream Life of Balso Snell
Nathanael West

These two novellas demonstrate the fragility of the American dream. In *The Day of the Locust*, talented young artist Todd Hackett has been brought to Hollywood to work in a major studio. He discovers a surreal world of tarnished dreams, where violence and hysteria lurk behind the glittering façade. 'The best of the Hollywood novels, a nightmare vision of humanity destroyed by its obsession with film' J. G. Ballard, *Sunday Times*

The Myth of Sisyphus Albert Camus

The Myth of Sisyphus is one of the most profound philosophical statements written this century. It is a discussion of the central idea of absurdity that Camus was to develop in his novel *The Outsider*. Here Camus poses the fundamental question – Is life worth living? – and movingly argues for an acceptance of reality that encompasses revolt, passion and, above all, liberty.

READ MORE IN PENGUIN

Published or forthcoming:

The Diary of a Young Girl Anne Frank

This definitive edition of Anne Frank's diary restores substantial material omitted from the original edition, giving us a deeper insight into her world. 'One of the greatest books of the twentieth century ... If you have never read Anne Frank's diary, or haven't read it for years, this is the edition to buy' *Guardian*

Brideshead Revisited Evelyn Waugh

The most nostalgic of Evelyn Waugh's novels, *Brideshead Revisited* looks back to the golden age before the Second World War. It tells the story of Charles Ryder's infatuation with the Marchmains and the rapidly disappearing world of privilege they inhabit. 'Lush and evocative ... expresses at once the profundity of change and the indomitable endurance of the human spirit' *The Times*

Oranges John McPhee

From Thailand, where the sweetest oranges are as green as emeralds, to Florida oranges so juicy it is said they should be peeled in the bath, the orange exists in bounteous varieties. John McPhee has woven together history, anecdote and science to create a definitive guide to the world of oranges. 'A classic of American reportage. McPhee is quirky, original and intensely curious' Julian Barnes

Wide Sargasso Sea Jean Rhys

Inspired by Charlotte Brontë's *Jane Eyre*, *Wide Sargasso Sea* is set in the lush landscape of Jamaica in the 1830s. Born into an oppressive colonialist society, Creole heiress Antoinette Cosway meets and marries a young Englishman. But as Antoinette becomes caught between his demands and her own precarious sense of belonging, she is eventually driven towards madness.

Published or forthcoming:

The Chrysalids John Wyndham

Genetic mutation has devastated the world. In the primitive society that has emerged from its ruins, any sign of deviation is ruthlessly hunted out and destroyed. David lives in fear of discovery, for he is part of a secret group who are able to communicate with each other through their thoughts. As they grow older they feel increasingly isolated. Then one of them marries a 'norm' with terrifying consequences.

The Waves Virginia Woolf

The Waves traces the lives of a group of friends from childhood to youth and middle age. While social events, individual achievements and disappointments form its narrative, the novel is most remarkable for the poetic language that conveys the inner life of its characters: their aspirations, their triumphs and regrets, their awareness of unity and isolation.

Heart of Darkness Joseph Conrad

In Conrad's haunting tale Marlow, a seaman and wanderer, recounts his journey to the heart of Africa in search of the enigmatic Kurtz. He discovers how Kurtz has gained his position of power over the local people, and radically questions not only his own nature and values, but those of his society. '*Heart of Darkness* seemed to reach into the heart of Conrad himself' Peter Ackroyd, *The Times*

The Garden Party and Other Stories Katherine Mansfield

Innovative, startlingly perceptive and aglow with colour, these fifteen stories were written towards the end of Katherine Mansfield's short life. Many are set in the author's native New Zealand, others in England and the French Riviera. All are revelations of the unspoken, half-understood emotions that make up everyday experience.

BY THE SAME AUTHOR

NOVELS

Aaron's Rod
Kangaroo
Lady Chatterley's Lover
Mr Noon

The Rainbow
Sons and Lovers
Women in Love

SHORT STORIES

Three Novellas: The Fox/
  The Ladybird/The Captain's
  Doll
The Complete Short Novels

The Virgin and the Gipsy
The Prussian Officer
St Mawr and Other Stories
Selected Short Stories

TRAVEL BOOKS AND OTHER WORKS

Studies in Classic
  American Literature
D. H. Lawrence and Italy
Sea and Sardinia

Sketches of Etruscan Places
Twilight in Italy
Apocalypse

POETRY

D. H. Lawrence: Selected Poetry
Edited and Introduced by Keith Sagar
Birds, Beasts and Flowers

Penguin are now publishing the Cambridge editions of D. H. Lawrence's texts. These are as close as can be determined to those he would have intended.

Sons and Lovers, read by Paul Copley, and *Women in Love*, read by Michael Maloney, are also available as Penguin Audiobooks.

PENGUIN STUDENT EDITIONS

Series Editors: Ronald Carter and John McRae

Penguin Student Editions have been specifically designed for readers who are studying a text in detail. They include a helpful introduction and explanatory notes, character sketches, a text summary, a chronology, language notes, a selection of questions and topics for discussion and analysis, as well as suggestions for further reading.

Also published:

Jane Austen	**Emma**
	Pride and Prejudice
William Boyd	**A Good Man in Africa**
Charlotte Brontë	**Jane Eyre**
Arthur Conan Doyle	**The Hound of the Baskervilles**
Roald Dahl	**Ten Short Stories**
Charles Dickens	**A Christmas Carol**
E. M. Forster	**A Passage to India**
Alex Garland	**The Beach**
Henry James	**The Turn of the Screw**
James Joyce	**Dubliners**
D. H. Lawrence	**The Fox and Other Stories**
Jack London	**The Call of the Wild**
Bernard Mac Laverty	**Cal**
Katherine Mansfield	**The Garden Party and Other Stories**
George Orwell	**Animal Farm**
	Nineteen Eighty-Four
Jean Rhys	**Wide Sargasso Sea**
Bernard Shaw	**Pygmalion**
Robert Louis Stevenson	**The Strange Case of Dr Jekyll and Mr Hyde**
H. G. Wells	**The Time Machine**
Oscar Wilde	**The Importance of Being Earnest**
	Lord Arthur Savile's Crime and Other Stories